The Rays of Light

LESLIE BASFORD, B.Sc. JOAN PICK, B.Sc.

FOUNDATIONS OF SCIENCE LIBRARY

GREYSTONE PRESS/NEW YORK • TORONTO • LONDON

This new presentation assembles freshly edited material from
'Understanding Science' on one subject into a single volume.

Copyright © MCMLXVI Sampson Low, Marston & Co. Ltd.

Library of Congress Catalog Card Number: 66–17978

Printed in Great Britain
Manufactured in U.S.A.

Contents

THE NATURE OF LIGHT . . . . . *page* 5

  1 THE NATURE OF LIGHT 6

  2 MEASURING THE VELOCITY OF LIGHT . . . 10

  3 MEASURING THE INTENSITY OF LIGHT . . . 14

AN INTRODUCTION TO MIRRORS AND LENSES . . . 17

  4 PLANE MIRRORS 18

  5 CURVED MIRRORS 21

  6 REFRACTION – THE BENDING OF LIGHT . . . 23

  7 MIRAGES 26

  8 LIGHT AND LENSES 28

IMAGES 31

  9 THE FORMATION OF IMAGES 32

  10 MIRROR AND LENS IMAGES 35

  11 FINDING THE FOCAL LENGTH . . . 39

  12 LENS COMBINATIONS 42

  13 THE OPTICAL BENCH 46

LENSES AND THEIR DEFECTS 49

  14 THE EYE AND ITS DEFECTS 50

  15 THE MANUFACTURE OF LENSES . . . 54

  16 THE BLOOMING OF LENSES 58

  17 DEFECTS OF LENSES 62

OPTICAL INSTRUMENTS . . . . . . *page* 65

   18 TELESCOPES 66

   19 THE COMPOUND MICROSCOPE 69

   20 DIASCOPES AND EPIDIASCOPES 72

   21 PRISMS AND PERISCOPES 74

   22 THE CAMERA 76

THE COLOURS OF LIGHT 81

   23 SPECTRA AND SPECTROSCOPES 82

   24 THE RAINBOW 87

   25 THE COLOUR OF THE SKY 89

   26 COLOUR FILTERS 91

   27 COLOUR MIXING 93

LIGHT WAVES IN ACTION 97

   28 INTERFERENCE 98

   29 FRESNEL'S BIPRISM 103

   30 INSPECTING SURFACES 105

   31 DIFFRACTION 108

   32 RAYLEIGH'S CRITERION 113

   33 THE PHASE CONTRAST MICROSCOPE . . 114

   34 POLARIZATION 119

PHOTO-ELECTRIC EFFECT 123

   35 THE PHOTO-ELECTRIC EFFECT . . . 124

      INDEX 128

The Nature of Light

CHAPTER ONE

The Nature of Light

AT one time, a ray of light was thought to be made up of millions of infinitesimally tiny particles, or *corpuscles*, travelling at enormous speeds. This had been deduced from the way light was reflected by mirrors. When a ray of light strikes the surface of a mirror, it 'bounces' off it in much the same way as a ball bounces off a wall. The angle at which it hits the wall (the angle of incidence) is exactly equal to the angle at which it bounces off again (the angle of reflection), provided that the ball is what is called 'perfectly elastic'.

Are light rays particles?

The *corpuscular* idea is perhaps the easiest way of visualizing a beam of light. The corpuscles travel in straight lines, for they tend to travel between two points taking the shortest possible route. Very hot objects, like the sun, or an electric light filament, would emit streams of tiny corpuscles. Other objects are seen because they reflect some of the corpuscles striking them. Human bodies emit no light corpuscles of their own, but they are made visible when they reflect corpuscles into the eyes of the person looking at them. According to the corpuscular theory, all the light energy reaching the Earth from the Sun is carried by corpuscles.

More modern theories on the nature of light suggest that light is indeed a collection of tiny particles, which are emitted by hot bodies like the Sun.

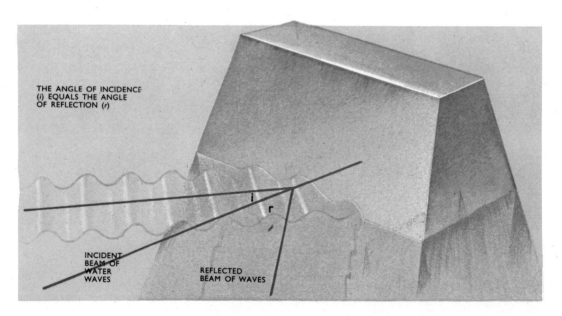

THE ANGLE OF INCIDENCE (i) EQUALS THE ANGLE OF REFLECTION (r)

i

r

INCIDENT BEAM OF WATER WAVES

REFLECTED BEAM OF WAVES

Waves, like particles, obey the laws of reflection. The beam of water waves is being reflected by the wall. It can be shown that light waves are reflected by mirrors in the same way.

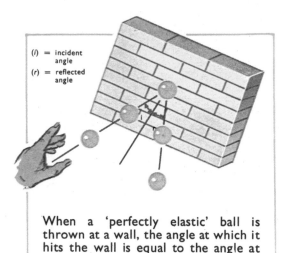

| (i) = incident angle |
| (r) = reflected angle |

When a 'perfectly elastic' ball is thrown at a wall, the angle at which it hits the wall is equal to the angle at which it bounces away.

IMAGE OF LAMP

MIRROR

LIGHT PARTICLES

In the same way, light 'corpuscles' bounce off the surface of a mirror. The angle of incidence is equal to the angle of reflection.

But the subtle difference between the modern light particle, *the photon*, and the older version, the *corpuscle*, is that the photon does not *carry* energy – it *is* energy.

A photon can be thought of as a minute bundle of energy. It is unlike any other kind of particle, for it exists only when it is moving. When it is travelling at its usual speed of around 186,000 miles per second, a photon can behave very much like an ordinary piece of matter. It can collide with particles, such as electrons and protons, and deflect them just as if it were an ordinary particle. In the photo-electric light meter used in photography, photons striking a piece of light-sensitive metal release electrons from the metal. The electrons form an electric current, which moves a pointer to indicate how strong the light is. It has been found that one electron is released by one photon. The electrons are particles, and they are freed by photons, behaving like particles.

Sir Isaac Newton was a supporter of the old corpuscular theory, and because of his influence, it held sway during the 18th century. The modern photon theory originated with Albert Einstein's work on the photo-electric effect in 1905. His investigations showed that electrons had been knocked away from their parent atoms by individual light particles. Light was not a continuous stream of energy, but instead discontinuous bundles of it.

Is light a wave?

Between the old corpuscular theory, and the newer photon theory, scientists argued that light was a continuous wave-like disturbance. In many ways, light waves were like water waves. They spread out from a disturbance in ever-increasing circles. There were successions of crests and troughs, and if two sets of waves happened to meet so that crest coincided with trough, the two waves would fill each other in and completely disappear. This effect, which is called *interference*, is quite easy to produce with water waves, but not quite so easy to see in light waves, because the waves – vibrations from side to side and up and down – are very small indeed.

The wave nature of light gives rise to other interesting properties. Light

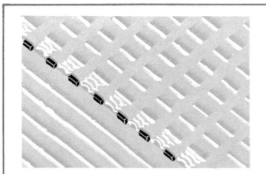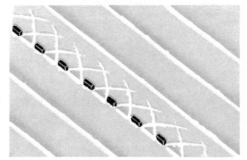

Waves are disturbed by large obstacles, and the disturbance carries on the other side (diagram on the left). But when the obstacles are small compared with the size of the wave, the waves can pass through them without being disturbed very much (diagram on the right). Light waves behave in a similar way.

travels in straight lines, and in fact the waves do travel forwards in straight lines. But at the same time they vibrate from side to side and up and down. They can sidle around the edges of opaque objects, and so bend into the area which ought to be in the shadow of the object. This phenomenon is called *diffraction*. It is very important in high-power microscopes, for if the object being magnified is about the same size as a light wave, light can sidle around the object, and the magnified image will be very distorted. The size of the light wavelength (about five hundred-thousandths of a centimetre) limits the size of object which can be magnified in a microscope using ordinary light.

Both interference and diffraction were observed during the 18th and 19th centuries. Scientists who saw

these effects argued quite rightly that they could not have been caused by corpuscles. They could have been caused only by a kind of wave.

Light rays are wave-like disturbances travelling at around 186,000 miles per second through space. They are disturbances like waves on water, or like sound waves, which are disturbances of air. Light waves are disturbances – but disturbances of what? It was thought that space was practically empty – there was nothing in space to disturb. It was inconceivable that disturbances of nothingness could be the means of transferring light from the Earth to the Sun. So a mysterious substance called *aether* was invented. *Aether* existed everywhere, and light was a disturbance of the aether. But *aether* has never been detected, and is never likely to be. For, to transmit light

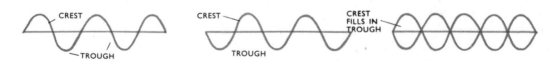

Above: A wave can be annihilated by another wave, if they meet so that the crests of one wave coincide with the troughs of the other wave. This is called interference.

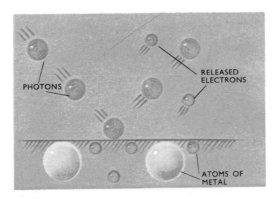

Light behaves like a stream of particles in the photo-electric effect, where it is found that one light-particle, or photon, can release one electron.

Waves spread out from a disturbance in ever-increasing circles. The distance between consecutive crests is called the wavelength.

waves through it at 186,000 miles per second, it must be endowed with remarkable properties. One of these is that it must be as rigid as steel!

It is now known that light waves are *electromagnetic waves*. They are very rapid variations in electric and magnetic fields, and fields can exist and vary in empty space. *Aether* is not necessary at all.

Light rays are wave-particles

Light is neither completely a wave, nor completely a particle. It is a cross between the two – a wave-particle. Sometimes light behaves like a wave (e.g. in interference and diffraction) and sometimes it behaves like a particle (e.g. in the photo-electric effect). This is a rather complicated theory, but it is the only one capable of explaining all aspects of light's behaviour. It is in line with modern theories about the nature of all matter, which is also thought to have both particle and wave properties. The bigger the particle, the less noticeable become the wave properties.

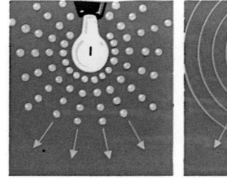

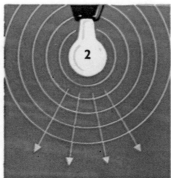

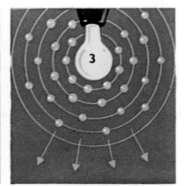

The two older theories on the nature of light, (1) the corpuscular theory and (2) the wave-theory have merged into the modern wave-particle theory (3). Light can behave either like a stream of particles, or like a train of waves.

CHAPTER TWO

Measuring the Velocity of Light

LIGHT travels at such a fantastic speed that it is impossible for the eye to detect its movement. In one second it travels approximately 186,000 miles. It only takes 1·3 seconds for light reflected from the moon to reach the Earth.

Because of the enormous distance travelled in the brief space of one second it is not surprising that the first attempts to find the speed of light failed. These were performed by Galileo who tried to find the time taken for light to travel from one person to another several miles away. Their errors in timing must have been far greater than the time they were attempting to measure.

The first reasonably accurate value was calculated by the Danish astronomer Olaus Röemer in 1676. He noticed that Io, a moon orbiting round the planet Jupiter was blocked from the Earth's view at certain intervals of time. These eclipses occurred when Io was behind Jupiter which stopped the light from reaching the Earth. When the Earth was nearest to Jupiter he calculated the times when he expected the eclipses to happen, but found that when the Earth was on the far side of the Sun the eclipses occurred some time later. He reasoned that the delay was due to the light's taking longer to travel the extra distance. As he knew the distance involved he was able to calculate the velocity of light.

It was not until almost 200 years later that Röemer's result was verified by the Frenchmen, Fizeau and Foucault. Fizeau in 1849, and Foucault in 1862, succeeded in measuring the velocity of light using comparatively short light paths. Neither made use of astronomy.

Fizeau's method. Fizeau used a toothed wheel to help him measure the time taken for light to travel 12 miles. A converging lens gathered up

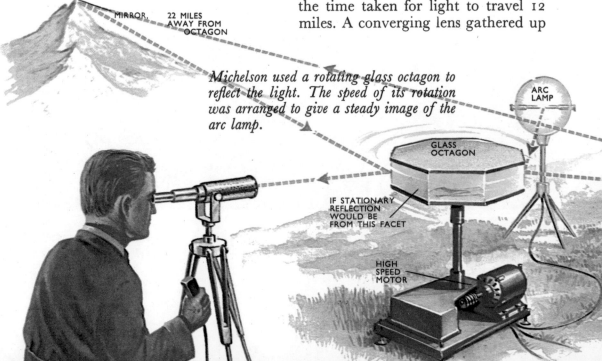

MIRROR, 22 MILES AWAY FROM OCTAGON

Michelson used a rotating glass octagon to reflect the light. The speed of its rotation was arranged to give a steady image of the arc lamp.

ARC LAMP

GLASS OCTAGON

IF STATIONARY REFLECTION WOULD BE FROM THIS FACET

HIGH SPEED MOTOR

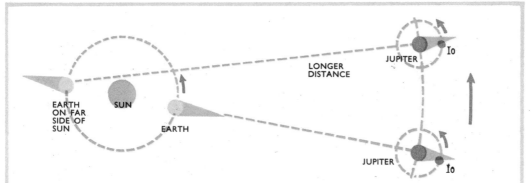

Röemer's method for finding the velocity of light. When Jupiter is a long way from the Earth its satellite, Io, eclipses later than would be expected. This is because the light takes more time to travel the extra distance.

the light rays from a powerful light source. A plate of glass was placed at an angle to these rays just before they would have been brought to a focus. Instead, the light rays were reflected and brought to a focus on one side of the glass plate. These rays were made parallel by a collimating lens placed so that the actual light focus coincided with the principal focus of the lens. The rays travelled in this parallel condition over a distance of about 6 miles before meeting yet another converging lens which brought them to a focus at a concave mirror placed so that the rays were reflected back along the same path and brought to a focus again by the first lens just before the glass plate. They passed through the glass plate and the image they formed (at the focus of the first lens) was viewed by Fizeau using an eyepiece. Fizeau had a wheel very

carefully cut so that it had 720 teeth spaced equally round its rim. The spaces between the teeth were exactly the same size as the teeth themselves. The rim of the wheel was placed so that a tooth could block off the outgoing and returning light at the light focus. It was then rotated, first slowly and then faster and faster until no light image could be seen through the eyepiece, only darkness. Outgoing light was passing through a gap between the teeth. This light travelled the 6 miles to the mirror and another 6 miles back, during which time the next tooth had moved into the space, blocking the image from the viewer. As he knew the distances involved and the speed at which the wheel was rotating, it was an easy step to calculate the velocity of light.

Foucault's Method. Foucault's apparatus was much simpler than Fizeau's and the light was timed over a much shorter distance. This had the advantage that the space could be filled with water or other transparent substances to find how fast light travelled through them. The space could also be evacuated to find the velocity of light in a vacuum. Light travels slightly more slowly in air

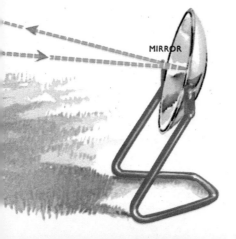

11

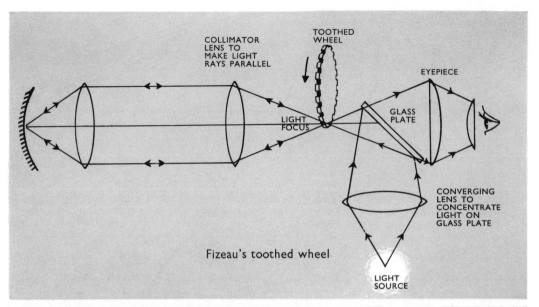

Fizeau's toothed wheel

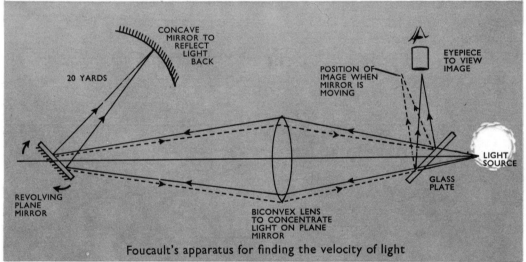

Foucault's apparatus for finding the velocity of light

than it does in a vacuum. It travels through water with only $\frac{3}{4}$ of its velocity in air. It travels through glass with an even smaller velocity. The actual velocity depends on the type of glass used.

Light from the source passes through a plate of glass and then through a converging lens which concentrates it onto the reflecting surface of a plane (flat) mirror. Another mirror, this time concave, is placed so that light reflected from the plane mirror is brought to focus on

its surface and reflected back along the same path by which it came. But when the light reaches the plate of glass, although some of it passes through, some is also reflected by its surface in just the same way that a glass window can give a reflection. These reflected light rays converge forming an image of the light source. This image is viewed through an eyepiece. Now the plane mirror is set rotating as fast as it can be made to move. When the light it reflects falls back on it, the mirror is in a different position and consequently the image viewed through the eyepiece is slightly shifted. The light speed can be worked out from the speed of rotation, the extent of the shift and the distances between the mirrors.

There are many modifications to this basic idea from which more accurate results have been found.

The largest error in Foucault's method lay in measuring the small shift made by the image. It would have been much better if he could have rotated the mirror so fast that it was back again in the same position to receive the returning light. This would give an image in the same position and only the speed of rotation and the distances between the two mirrors would be needed to calculate the velocity of light. Michelson overcame this problem by replacing the plane mirror by a glass octagon. Different facets of the octagon reflected the light on both its outward and return journeys. Hence light could only reach the observer when the octagon was in one particular position. This would be the case if the octagon were stationary or if it were rotating at such a speed that one facet exactly replaced the next while the light was travelling over its measured path to a distant reflector and back again. The speed of rotation which fulfils this condition could be found accurately and used in calculating the velocity of light.

Although light travels so very quickly, it still takes a considerable time for it to travel through the vastness of space. In fact some light arriving at the Earth may have come from stars or planets which have disappeared long ago, in which case it is possible to see something after it has completely disappeared.

Distances across space are so very vast that to express them in terms of miles would be ridiculous. The number of noughts would probably fill a page. Instead, large astronomical distances can be measured in *light years*. A light year is the distance that light travels through empty space in 1 year. If it travels approximately 186,000 miles in every second, then in a year it will travel this distance in miles multiplied by the number of seconds in a year. A light year, then, is approximately 5,870,000,000,000 miles.

Nothing has been known to travel faster than light. Although scientists may try to make things move faster and faster, it is extremely unlikely that they will ever be able to make any material thing even approach the speed of light. As its speed increases, its mass also increases and this gain in mass hinders it from travelling faster.

CHAPTER THREE

Measuring the Intensity of Light

THE Sun is a much stronger source of light than a weakly flickering candle; so is a powerful electric light bulb, although its intensity is negligible compared with that of the Sun.

Photometry is the branch of science in which the intensities of different sources of light are compared one with another. If the actual intensity of one light source is known, then the other can be calculated.

There is no obvious unit for measuring the intensities of light sources. It is therefore necessary to agree on a *standard* source with which other sources can be compared. The original standard was simply a candle. A standard candle made in a particular shape and of a certain type of wax, burning away at a certain rate, was agreed to be a light source of one *candle-power*. A source ten times as intense would be rated at ten candle-power. As the old standard wax candles were not particularly accurate, they were replaced by standard lamps burning pentane under specified conditions. Pentane lamps were superseded as standards by electric lamps of special construction, but the term 'candle-power' was and is still used. The present-day standard unit is the *candela*. This is based on the light emitted from a small hole in the lid of a crucible filled with molten platinum. One candela is roughly equal to one candle-power.

If a large room is illuminated by only one light, the obvious place in which to read a book is almost underneath the light (directly underneath would be better if it were not for the book falling in the shadow). In this position, the book is well *illuminated*, but in the far corner of the room it may well be that the book is so dimly illuminated that it is impossible to read. The *illumination* of the surface decreases with the distance from the light source even though the *luminous intensity* of the source remains the same.

Illumination is measured in terms of foot-candles. If a surface is placed one foot away from a one candle-power lamp in such a way that the light falls perpendicularly upon it, then that surface has an illumination of one foot-candle. Two feet away from the light source, the illumination would only be $\frac{1}{4}$ foot-candle; 3 feet away only $\frac{1}{9}$ and 4 feet away $\frac{1}{16}$ of a foot-candle. The illumination falls off as the square of the distance, i.e. distance $\times$ distance.

Illumination, then, is dependent upon two factors—the candle-power of the light source and the distance

The grease spot in the centre of the paper disc allows more light to pass through it than it reflects, whereas the ungreased paper reflects more light than it transmits. If the two sides are evenly illuminated, the grease spot stands out as a luminous spot on one side and a dark spot on the other. With the lamps in the correct positions, the grease spot cannot be distinguished from the paper. Mirrors enable both sides to be seen at once.

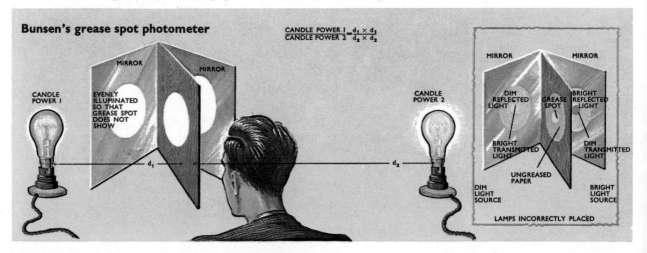

Bunsen's grease spot photometer

$$\frac{\text{CANDLE POWER 1}}{\text{CANDLE POWER 2}} = \frac{d_1 \times d_1}{d_2 \times d_2}$$

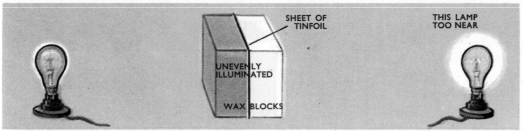

Joly's wax block photometer

The photometer consists of two rectangular wax blocks placed side by side and separated from each other by a sheet of tinfoil. Light from the sources falling upon the blocks makes them appear suffused with light. The positions of the sources are adjusted until the wax blocks appear to have the same brightness.

that the surface is from that light source. The illumination of a surface (i.e. the amount of light falling per second on each unit of its area) is related to the intensity of the light source by the equation:

Illumination of surface
$$= \frac{\text{candle-power of source}}{\text{distance} \times \text{distance}}$$

If distances are measured in feet, the illumination of surface given by this equation is expressed in foot-candles. This equation is used when the intensities of two light sources are being compared using a *photometer*.

Although there are many different types of photometer, all of them are devices which use two lamps (usually one of known candle-power and the other whose candle-power is being found). These lamps are arranged to illuminate two surfaces. The distances of the lamps from the illuminated surfaces are adjusted until both surfaces have the same illumination. The distances are measured and the candle-power of the unknown light source can be calculated.

$$\frac{\text{Known c-p.}}{(\text{distance})^2} = \frac{\text{unknown c-p.}}{(\text{its distance})^2}$$

On the other hand, if the two light sources are just being compared and neither candle-power is known, then their *ratio* is given by

$$\frac{\text{c-p. (light}_1)}{\text{c-p. (light}_2)} = \frac{\text{distance}^2 \text{ (light}_1)}{\text{distance}^2 \text{ (light}_2)}$$

If the two light sources are of the same colour, it is immaterial which type of photometer is used; but the human eye is incapable of judging

Rumford's shadow photometer

The two light sources throw shadows of an upright object onto the screen. The light sources are arranged so that the shadows do not overlap but just come side by side. When the sources are correctly positioned, both shadows are equally dark and appear to be not two separate shadows, but one large one. Calculations are similar to those for Bunsen's grease spot experiment.

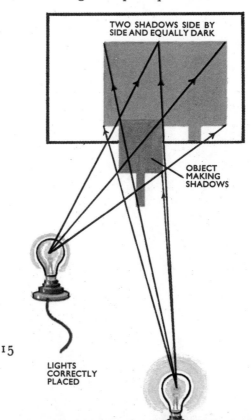

TWO SHADOWS SIDE BY SIDE AND EQUALLY DARK

OBJECT MAKING SHADOWS

LIGHTS CORRECTLY PLACED

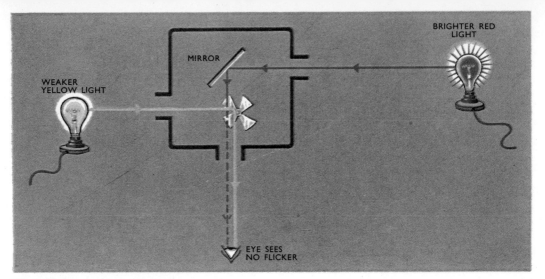

The flicker photometer

This photometer can be used to compare light sources of different colours. Light is viewed alternately from each source. Here, the light from the yellow source is reflected by the vanes on the wheel and red light is reflected by the mirror when the vanes are not blocking its path. The positions of the sources are adjusted until the experimenter does not see a flicker.

accurately when two surfaces are equally illuminated with lights of different colours. In this special case, most photometers are useless. The only type which can be used successfully is the *flicker* photometer. This consists of a wheel with four vanes on it. The vanes are the same size as the

Lummer—Brodhun photometer

Light from the two sources is directed by the mirror system onto two 90° prisms that are 'cemented' together as shown. Light from one source emerges from the centre of a prism, whereas light from the other source comes from the edges. The light sources are adjusted to make the prism seem evenly illuminated.

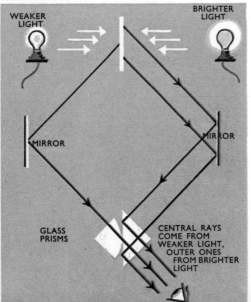

spaces between them. This wheel spins about 20 times every second. The vanes reflect light from one light source out to the observer. When the vanes are not in a position to do this, light from the other source is reflected out to the observer by a suitably placed matt white reflector. The observer sees first light from one source and then light from the other. If the sources are wrongly placed then the light flickers. With the lamps placed so that they produce equal illumination on the reflectors, the flickering ceases.

All these methods are methods of comparison. With the light meter (foot-candle meter) the illumination of a surface can be read off directly from a pointer moving over a calibrated dial. The light falls on a photo-cell in the meter and stimulates it to produce an electric current. The strength of this current depends upon the intensity of the light falling on it. A galvanometer within the meter measures the current, and the scale of the galvanometer is marked off to read directly in foot-candles.

16

An Introduction
to Mirrors and Lenses

CHAPTER FOUR

Plane Mirrors

EVERY surface reflects light to some extent. A piece of white paper, for example, absorbs about a fifth of the light falling on it and reflects back the remaining four-fifths. The light reflected from white paper is scattered in all directions. A mirror, on the other hand, reflects

The picture of the actor seen in the mirror is a true reflection. He is touching his moustache with his right hand; the mirror seems to show it as his left hand.

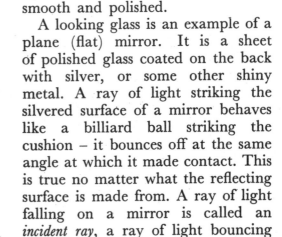

light *evenly* because its surface is smooth and polished.

A looking glass is an example of a plane (flat) mirror. It is a sheet of polished glass coated on the back with silver, or some other shiny metal. A ray of light striking the silvered surface of a mirror behaves like a billiard ball striking the cushion – it bounces off at the same angle at which it made contact. This is true no matter what the reflecting surface is made from. A ray of light falling on a mirror is called an *incident ray*, a ray of light bouncing off a mirror is called a *reflected ray*. The direction of a ray is measured not by the angle it makes with the mirror but by the angle it makes with a line (called the *normal*) drawn at right angles to the mirror. The normal is usually drawn through the point on the mirror's surface where the reflection takes place.

A very simple law holds good for all regular reflections. It states that the angle of incidence (i) between the incident ray and the normal, is always equal to the angle of reflection (r) between the reflected ray and the normal.

When you look into an ordinary flat mirror you see a reflection of yourself. It is the same shape and the same size and appears to be as far behind the mirror as you are in front. The reflection of anything we see in a mirror is called an *image*.

Why does a mirror form an image? The rays spreading out from an object

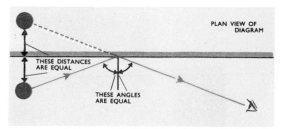

Why the image appears as far behind the mirror as the object is in front. Rays from the object falling on the mirror are always turned so that the angle of incidence equals the angle of reflection.

are turned through an angle by the mirror and continue to spread out even though they have suffered a change of direction. As a result, the direction in which the reflected rays reach our eyes does not lead straight to the object. It leads to a point *behind* the mirror, from which the rays *appear* to be coming. This point is the position of the image. It lies as far behind the mirror as the object is in front. Of course, it is easy to prove that there is really nothing behind the mirror: the image is a kind of optical illusion. It is said to be a 'virtual' or unreal image.

With two mirrors placed together at an angle, each of them produces an image of an object placed between them. But if the angle is narrow enough images of the images can be seen! Light rays from the direct image bounce off the opposite mirror and back into the observer's eye, forming extra images. As the angle between the mirrors narrows a greater number of images can be seen. A kaleidoscope consists of a tube in which two mirrors are arranged at an angle of 60° to each other. At the bottom of the tube are a number of pieces of coloured metal. Each has two images (one in each mirror), but these reflections are repeated a number of times, forming an intricate, symmetrical pattern

which can be changed simply by shaking the kaleidoscope and changing the positions of the pieces of metal. There are so many possibilities that you could never obtain the same pattern twice.

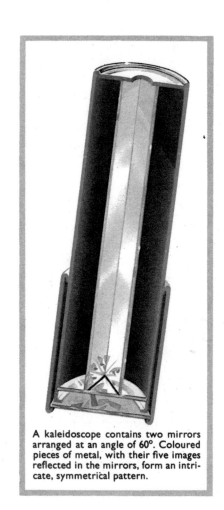

A kaleidoscope contains two mirrors arranged at an angle of 60°. Coloured pieces of metal, with their five images reflected in the mirrors, form an intricate, symmetrical pattern.

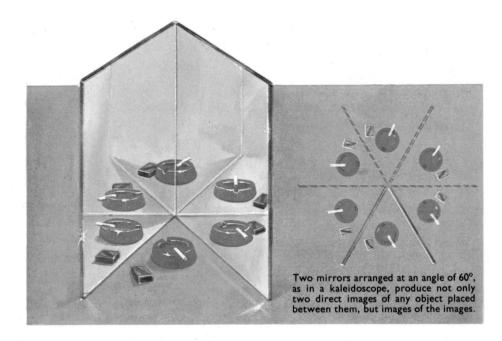

Two mirrors arranged at an angle of 60°, as in a kaleidoscope, produce not only two direct images of any object placed between them, but images of the images.

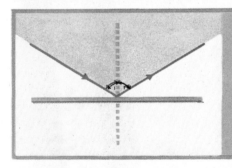

The angle at which a billiard ball strikes the cushion is equal to the angle at which it bounces off. Both these angles are in the same plane.

The incident angle (i) the angle between the incident ray and the normal is equal to the reflected angle (r) (the angle between the reflected ray and the normal).

angle i = angle r

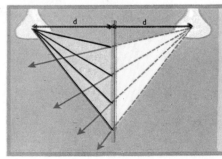

Rays of light turned by the mirror *appear* to be coming from behind the glass. All the rays converge at a point which is exactly as far behind the mirror as the object is in front of it.

CHAPTER FIVE

Curved Mirrors

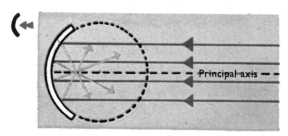

AN ORDINARY flat (plane) mirror can only give an image that is the same size as the object. The image is always upright and it always appears to be behind the mirror. It can never be caught on a screen because it is an unreal or *virtual* image. *Curved* mirrors, on the other hand, can produce images which are magnified or diminished, upright or upside down, real or unreal.

The most important types of curved mirrors are the *concave* (like the bowl of a spoon) and the *convex* (like the bulging back of a spoon). Both types can be cut from a hollow glass sphere—the difference depends on which side of the glass is silvered to make a reflecting surface.

A ray of light striking a plane mirror behaves like a ball striking the side of a billiard table—it bounces off at an angle equal to that at which it made contact. Now exactly the same thing happens with a curved mirror, for a curved mirror may be imagined as being made up of count-less tiny plane mirrors. But each of the plane mirrors is facing in a slightly different direction to its neighbours so that the rays in a parallel beam are reflected through different angles depending on where they strike the mirror.

A *concave* mirror gathers up rays of light falling on it and can even bring them to a point. Because of this, a concave mirror can make rays converge to form a real image. Real images are always upside down. If

When light rays, travelling parallel to the principal axis of a concave mirror are reflected, all pass through one point, known as the principal focus.

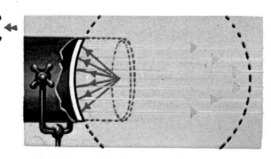

Searchlights and car headlights use concave mirrors. A light source is placed at the principal focus and those rays which strike the mirror are reflected as a parallel beam.

Many shaving mirrors are based upon the fact that if you stand near a concave mirror the image of your face will be larger than life.

the object is a long way from the mirror the image is reduced in size and appears about half way between the mirror and its *centre of curvature* (the centre of the sphere from which the mirror was cut). The point half way between the mirror and the centre of curvature is called the *principal focus*.

A beam of light from a very distant object (in which all the rays are parallel) converges onto the principal focus. Rays from the Sun, for example, are converged to form a small image that appears as a bright spot of light on a piece of white paper held in front of the mirror at its principal focus. This is put to good use in the reflecting telescope (although the mirrors used as reflectors are not exactly spherical). The small inverted image formed in the telescope is magnified by a system of lenses.

If an object is placed between a concave mirror and its principal focus the image is formed behind the mirror. It is, of course, an unreal or virtual image, since rays of light cannot pass through a mirror. The virtual image is upright and magnified. A concave mirror is used in this manner as a shaving mirror.

A *convex* mirror can only give one kind of image. No matter where the object is situated its image in a convex mirror is always upright, diminished and unreal. Driving mirrors are convex so that rays from a very wide area are reflected to the driver's eye—his field of view is increased because he sees a larger number of smaller images.

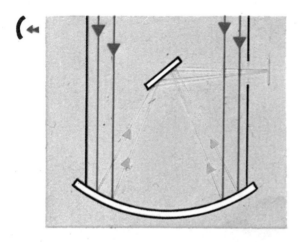

The Newtonian telescope. Light rays from a distant object strike the concave mirror at the bottom of the tube and are reflected towards the principal focus. Near the focus they strike a small flat mirror which reflects them out through the side of the tube to the eyepiece.

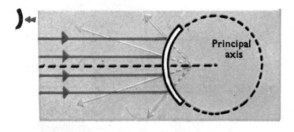

When light rays, travelling parallel to the principal axis of a convex mirror are reflected they diverge. But all appear to originate from a point behind the mirror— an imaginary focal point.

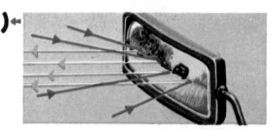

Some driving mirrors are convex. They gather in light from a wide surrounding area and direct the rays to the driver's eye. In this way he can see a diminished image of the whole road behind him.

CHAPTER SIX

Refraction – the Bending of Light

GENERALLY speaking, we cannot see round corners, because light travels in straight lines. There are, however, exceptions to the rule. The direction of light rays can, for example, be changed with a mirror. Light rays can also be bent under certain circumstances, a principle known as *refraction*.

Refraction of light can easily be seen at work. A straight stick or reed in a pond appears to be bent below the water line. A basin full of water appears shallower than when it is empty. In these examples the light has to travel through two substances (air and water). It is the changing over from one substance to the other which causes the light rays to bend. Air and water have different properties in respect to light. Light travels through air faster than it does through water. (Water is said to be '*optically denser*' than air.) Light rays travelling through air, meeting the surface of the water at an angle, are suddenly slowed down, and bent in the process. It is interesting to note that light which meets the water surface along a *normal* is *not* bent. (A *normal* is a line at right-angles to the surface.)

Which Way the Light Bends

The greater the difference between

The coin and cup trick. A coin is put at the bottom of an empty cup, just out of sight of the viewer. The coin is out of sight because a straight line (ray of light) cannot be drawn between eye and coin. When the cup is filled with water the viewer can see the coin, still in the same place at the bottom of the cup. This is because the light rays from the coin have been bent at the water surface so that they do enter the eye.

23

case the light rays are bent *away* from the normal. Where light passes from a less dense to a denser substance the rays are bent *towards* the normal. All this seems rather complicated. How does it work out in fact? The experiment with the torch and the fluorescent water pictured opposite shows light rays travelling through the air into water. Because slits are used to cast shadows we can follow the line of rays, noting that they change direction on hitting the surface of the water. Now take just one of the rays and see how it bends. If we were to draw in the normal (line at right-angles to the water surface) through the point where ray meets water we should see that the ray bends *towards* the normal. This is because the water has a greater optical density than the air. On reversing the experiment and passing the light rays from the water to the less dense air, the light bends *away* from the line of the normal. The effect of the glass walls of the tank used in these experiments can be ignored.

The Index of Refraction

The amount of bending which takes place as a ray of light passes from one substance to another with a different optical density can be expressed as an *index of refraction*. This is really a ratio or comparison of the speed of light through the two substances. The speed of light in air is about 186,000 miles per second and in water is about 139,500 miles per second. The ratio (index of refraction between air and water) is therefore 186,000/139,500 or roughly 4/3. The higher this index, the greater the angle through which the light is bent. So diamond, which has an index of about 2.42 compared to air, will bend the light passed from air far more than water will.

A fisherman shooting a fish must allow for the effects of refraction. Because of the bending of the light rays from the fish it appears to be farther away than it actually is. To hit the fish, therefore, the archer must aim below his target. Needless to say, the fisherman in this picture will miss because he is aiming at the apparent position of his target.

the optical densities of the two materials, the more the light will bend as it passes from one to the other. But *which way* the light bends depends on whether the light passes from a dense to a less dense material or the other way round. In the former

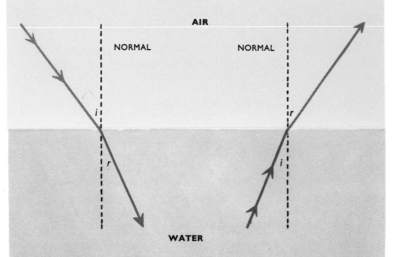

Refraction of light (*left*) from air to water and (*right*) from water to air. When the rays pass from air to water the angle of incidence (i) is greater than the angle of refraction (r). Where light travels from water to air the angle of incidence (i) is less than the angle of refraction (r).

Refraction problems

Most problems on refractive index can be solved simply from the equation

$$\frac{\sin i}{\sin r} = \text{refractive index}$$

Light rays passing from a substance to one that is optically denser are refracted (bent) *towards* the normal. Light rays passing from a substance to one that is optically less dense are refracted *away from* the normal. Light rays passing from one substance to another at right angles to the boundary are not refracted at all.

In this illustration light from a flash-light is passed through a 'comb' to show the direction of its rays more clearly. The light is then passed at an angle into a trough of water containing a fluorescent dye. If the room is darkened the dye shows up the direction of the light rays as fluorescent bands of light. For simplicity the light is not shown emerging from the sides of the trough.

When a narrow, well-defined beam of light strikes the side of the block of glass, some of the light is reflected.

The rest, which is refracted towards the normal passes on through the glass. At the other side of the block, some of the light is reflected, and the rest passes on into the air, being refracted away from the normal.

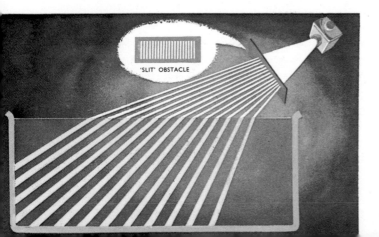

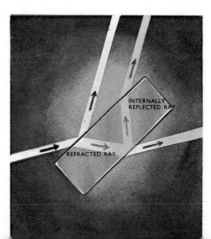

CHAPTER SEVEN

Mirages

WHEN rays of light pass at an angle from one transparent substance to another they are bent or *refracted*. This always happens when one of the substances is optically denser than the other, i.e. light travels less quickly in one than the other. For example light passing from air to water is slowed down, and is bent *towards* the normal (a line at right-angles to the water surface). Light passing from water to air is speeded up and is bent *away from* the normal. The angle a light ray in

certain amount of reflection always takes place from a surface when refraction takes place through it and the amount of light reflected increases with the angle of incidence until the critical angle is reached. Above this point *all* of the light is reflected.

Total internal reflection is easy to demonstrate with the aid of an underwater lamp. If an observer stands above the surface of the water in such a position that light rays from the lamp must strike the boundary

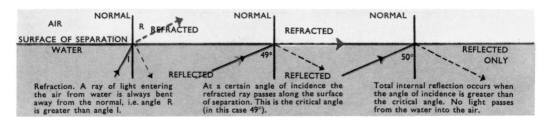

Refraction. A ray of light entering the air from water is always bent away from the normal, i.e. angle R is greater than angle I.

At a certain angle of incidence the refracted ray passes along the surface of separation. This is the critical angle (in this case 49°).

Total internal reflection occurs when the angle of incidence is greater than the critical angle. No light passes from the water into the air.

water makes with the normal is always less than the angle the light ray in air makes with the normal. Thus there must be a certain angle at which light rays travelling in water will, after refraction, pass directly along the surface. The angle at which this happens is called the *critical angle*. For water the critical angle is 49°, for glass 42°, and so on. When the angle of incidence (the angle at which the light rays strike the surface of separation, measured from the normal) is greater than the critical angle the light ray does not enter the second substance (e.g. air) at all; instead, it is reflected. A

between the water and the air at an angle greater than the critical angle in order to reach his eye, he will be unable to see the lamp. The light rays travelling in his direction will never leave the water; they will be *reflected* from the surface of separation between the water and the air.

Mirages are examples of total internal reflection. The conditions most likely to produce a mirage in the desert would be a layer of hot air lying immediately above the ground with cooler air above it (this is quite usual during the day because the ground becomes so hot). Light rays from a distant object, e.g. a tree,

would travel in a straight line through the cool air to an observer's eye. But other light rays from the tree would travel towards the ground and come in contact with the surface of separation between the cool and the hot air with their different optical densities. The rays which struck this surface very obliquely (at an angle greater than the critical angle) would be reflected upwards again and thus reach the observer's eye. In this way the observer would see the distant tree not only upright but also inverted, as though mirrored in a pool of water. You can see a similar effect on heated roads during the summer. The reflection of the sky and clouds appears just above the surface of the road as though mirrored in a pool of water. This is known as an *inferior mirage*.

More spectacular mirages are the type sometimes seen at sea. They may take the form of a ship floating in the air, or the lights of a distant city shining in the sky. The conditions needed to produce this kind of mirage (*superior mirage*) are exactly opposite to those needed in the previous case. It requires a thick layer of cold air lying above the surface of the sea with warmer air above it. The light rays from the ship which travel

An inferior mirage often to be seen on a hot summer day. The sky and clouds appear to be reflected in a pool of water on the road ahead. This is caused by heated air lying immediately above the road. As you drive towards it the 'pool of water' disappears.

upwards and strike the surface of separation between the cold and warm air at an angle greater than the critical angle are reflected back into the eye of the distant observer. In this way an observer may see a ship mirrored in the sky, though the actual ship may be out of sight, hidden by the curve of the Earth.

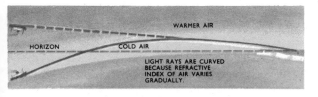

CHAPTER EIGHT

Light and Lenses

TO all sorts of optical instruments lenses are essential. There would be no microscopes without them, no film cameras, nor film projectors. In fact a natural lens forms an important part of every human eye. A lens can do two things with light rays. It can concentrate or disperse them, and, more important, it can form them into a replica (image) of any object which emits or reflects light rays. Refraction makes this possible.

When light passes at an angle through a window pane it does not seem to change its direction. What happens is that the light is bent upon entering the glass and bent again upon leaving it, but the light ray is displaced so little that it is not noticeable (in the first case the light is bent towards the normal and in the second case away from it). This is where a *lens* differs from a pane of glass: it is shaped in such a way that instead of the two bendings cancelling each other out, one reinforces the other and so the direction of the light is changed.

A double convex lens is a piece of glass or other transparent material which presents two bulging faces, *i.e.*, it is fatter in the middle than at the

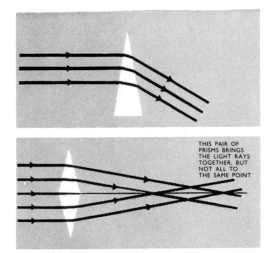

THIS PAIR OF PRISMS BRINGS THE LIGHT RAYS TOGETHER, BUT NOT ALL TO THE SAME POINT

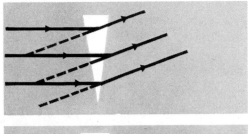

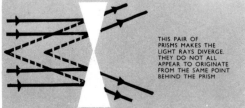

THIS PAIR OF PRISMS MAKES THE LIGHT RAYS DIVERGE. THEY DO NOT ALL APPEAR TO ORIGINATE FROM THE SAME POINT BEHIND THE PRISM

When light enters a prism it is bent slightly at the first surface, and then bent again at the second surface. Both the bendings are in the same direction, so they reinforce each other. The rays are bent away from the pointed end of the prism, towards its shortest side.

Light rays are bent inwards when they pass through two very thin prisms stuck together at their shortest sides. A parallel beam of light hitting the prism is focused by the pair of prisms into a not very precise bundle of light. All the rays are bent in the same direction, but they are not all brought to a focus at the same point.

edges. A source of light sends out light rays in all directions. The diagram shows what happens when a source of light is placed near a double convex lens. Those light rays which strike the lens and pass through it are bent towards each other, *i.e.*, they converge. The point at which they meet is called a *focus*. If a piece of white paper were to be placed at the focus a bright spot of light would appear upon it.

A double concave lens is a piece of glass which presents two hollow faces, *i.e.*, it is thinner in the middle than at the edges. If a source of light is placed near a double concave lens, those rays which strike the lens and pass through it will be bent away from each other, *i.e.*, they will diverge. There is very little practical use in weakening light in this way, but concave lenses are in fact very useful in optical instruments for adjusting the effect of convex lenses.

The 'burning-glass' is a double

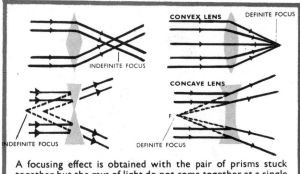

A focusing effect is obtained with the pair of prisms stuck together but the rays of light do not come together at a single focus. By curving the surface of the prisms lenses are formed and a single focal point (F) is obtained.

convex lens. Rays of light passing through it converge and meet at the focus. But the Sun's rays are accompanied by infra-red (heat) rays and these, too, are focused by the lens in a similar manner. So if a burning-glass is held up to the Sun, and a piece of paper is placed so that the light rays are focused upon it as a bright spot, the invisible heat rays will also be focused at that point and the paper will char.

If a marble, say, is placed in front of a double convex lens instead of a source of light the result is very similar. The spherical marble reflects in all directions light falling upon it. Those rays which strike the lens and pass through it are bent towards each other and brought to a focus. If a piece of paper were to be placed at this point an image of the marble would appear upon it (provided that the marble is brightly illuminated).

Defects in Lenses

One important defect of the simple convex lens, which arises from the spherical shape of its faces, is that it produces a blurred image. This is

Types of Lenses

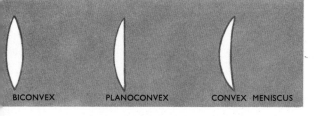

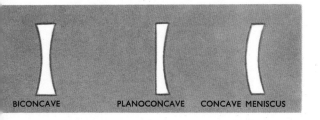

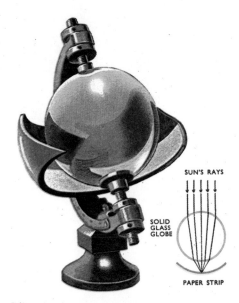

The Sun's rays are focused by the glass globe of the sunshine recorder and will char a piece of paper. From the length of the charred trace, the hours of sunshine can be calculated.

the same spot. This defect could be overcome by altering the shape of the lens slightly. The difficulty here is that the very way in which lenses are made (grinding by revolving abrasive pads) means that their surface must be spherical. The usual method of minimising spherical aberration is to prevent the light passing through the edges of the lens

These are the glass blanks from which lenses are made. They are ground and polished to make lenses. Great care is taken that they are of the standard required.

known as *spherical aberration*. It is due to the fact that a lens bends light rays that pass near its edge more than those which pass near its centre. So light rays reflected from an object striking the lens at different points are not focused onto exactly

where the excessive bending takes place. Another common defect in lenses is *chromatic aberration*. This is caused by the fact that a lens brings light of different wavelengths to focus at different points. A coloured image can result.

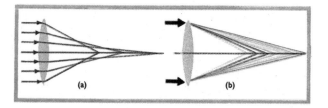

Two common defects in lenses: (a) Spherical aberration; (b) Chromatic aberration.

Images

CHAPTER NINE

The Formation of Images

AN observer looking into a mirror sees an *image* of himself. He is the 'object' that has caused the image. But if he reaches out to touch it he can only feel the surface of the glass stopping him from reaching the image. For the image appears to be behind the glass. Of course there is nothing really there: it is an optical illusion. How is such an image formed?

An object is visible if it gives out light (as, for example, a lamp gives out light), or if rays from a source of light bounce off the object (as, for example, rays of light bounce off white paper). Whether the object is actually giving out light, or merely reflecting back the light falling on it, rays of light spread out from every point on the object. An observer *sees* the object if some of the rays enter his eyes.

If, in some way, light rays can be *bent* from their direct paths the eye sees the object all right, but *not in its true position*. The rays seem to be spreading out from some point beyond the object. What the eye sees is the point from which the rays reaching it *appear* to have come. (The eye and the brain do not realise that the rays have

in fact been bent from their direct paths.) So it is a kind of optical illusion—the object has not moved to a new position. The eye is looking at an *image*.

How are the rays made to bend? Rays can be bent in a number of ways. The simplest is reflection by a plane (flat) mirror. Each of the rays obeys the law of reflection, in other words the angle of incidence equals the angle of reflection. If the rays bouncing off the mirror into the eye are traced back, they appear to be spreading out from a point behind the mirror. There is in fact nothing at the point from where the rays appear to be coming. The *image* is said to be unreal, imaginary, or *virtual*. By making a scaled drawing of the paths of two or three rays from a point on the object to the mirror, and thence to the eye (drawing the angle of reflection equal to the angle of incidence), it is possible to trace back the rays to the point from which they *appear* to come. This is a point on the image. It is as far *behind* the mirror as the corresponding point on the object is in front of the mirror. Curved mirrors can also produce images like those pro-

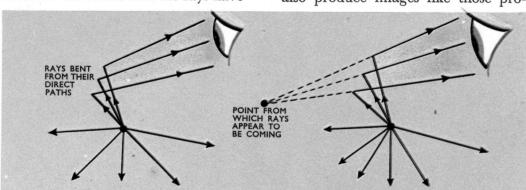

If light rays can be bent from their direct paths, the eye sees the object, but not in its true position.

The eye and the brain do not realize that the rays have been bent from their direct paths. The eye sees a kind of optical illusion. The point from which the rays appear to be spreading is a point on the image.

duced by a plane mirror. Again the rays must obey the laws of reflection. But the distance from the image to the curved mirror is not equal to the distance from the mirror to the object. And with curved mirrors the image may be larger or smaller than the object. (Drawing a few rays from one point on the object, however, cannot show the *size* of the image.)

A very different way of making light rays bend, and thus giving rise to an image, is with the aid of a lens. Rays are bent, or *refracted*, as they enter the lens and as they leave it. A converging lens, as its name suggests, gathers up light rays. But it cannot always bring the rays together to make them meet (i.e. it cannot always focus them). Rays spreading out from any point on an object placed very close to a converging lens will still be spreading out after passing through the lens. But their paths have been altered on entering and leaving the lens. If the rays entering the eye are traced back they apparently come from a point behind the object. This is the point which the eye sees: it is a point on the image. Once again this kind of image is an optical illusion because light rays

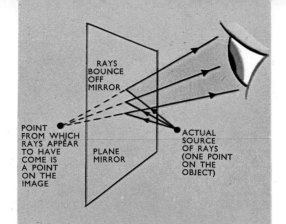

Reflection by a plane mirror diverts the rays from their direct paths. This gives the illusion of an image as far behind the mirror as the object is in front. For clarity only three rays have been drawn in the diagram.

do not in fact come from the image. The image is virtual (as a matter of interest it is also bigger than the object—it is the image formed by a magnifying glass).

A diverging lens always gives rise to virtual images. Rays of light spreading out from any point on an object are spread out even more by the diverging lens and their paths are altered as they enter and leave the lens. If the rays are traced back they apparently come from a point in front of the object. The image is always virtual (and as a matter of interest always diminished).

All the images mentioned so far

A converging lens will give rise to a *real* image of any object placed a long way from it. Rays of light from a point on the object cross and the eye receives rays of light spreading out from the point where they cross. The eye sees an image at the point where the rays cross. The image is formed on the opposite side of the lens from the object.

A concave mirror will give rise to a real image of any object placed a long way from it. Rays of light from a point on the object cross, and the eye receives rays of light from the point where they cross. The eye sees an image at the point where they cross. The image is formed on the same side of the mirror as the object.

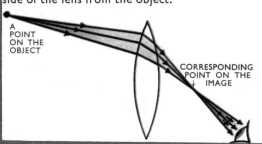

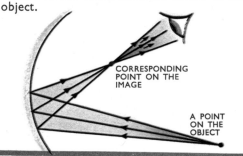

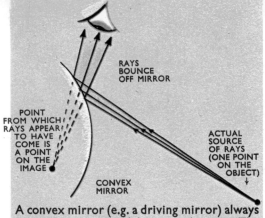

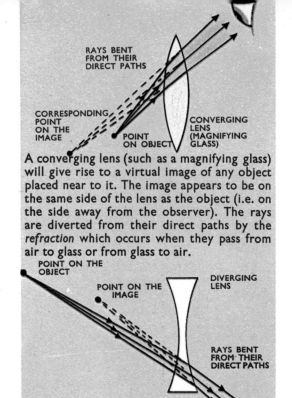

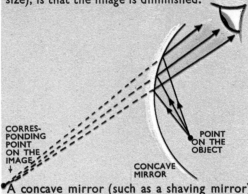

A convex mirror (e.g. a driving mirror) always gives rise to a virtual (imaginary) image. The rays must still obey the law of reflection. What this diagram cannot show (since it is concerned with point objects that have no size), is that the image is diminished.

A converging lens (such as a magnifying glass) will give rise to a virtual image of any object placed near to it. The image appears to be on the same side of the lens as the object (i.e. on the side away from the observer). The rays are diverted from their direct paths by the *refraction* which occurs when they pass from air to glass or from glass to air.

A concave mirror (such as a shaving mirror) will give rise to a virtual image of any object placed near to it. The image appears to be behind the mirror.

A diverging lens always gives rise to a virtual image no matter where the object is situated. The image is always on the same side of the lens as the object.

have been virtual. They exist only in imagination. If a piece of paper is placed at the point where the image is seen, nothing appears on the paper. But converging lenses and concave mirrors are capable of forming *real* images—images which can be caught on a piece of paper just as the image formed by a projector is caught on the cinema screen.

Rays spreading out from any point on an object placed a long way from a converging lens are gathered up. They are gathered up so drastically that they all meet at one point. However they do not stop when they meet, they cross and continue on their way to the observer. But since they have crossed they are spreading out again. Rays reaching the eye actually do

spread out from the point where they have crossed and the eye sees an image at this point. The image is *real* because real rays of light spread out from it. A piece of paper placed at the point where the rays meet would catch the image (providing the object was either giving out, or reflecting enough light). Real images formed in this way are always upside-down (inverted) because of the crossing-over of light rays.

A concave mirror produces real images of objects placed a long way from it in much the same way as a converging lens produces real images. In the case of the mirror, of course, the paths of the rays are changed by *reflection*, in the case of the lens the paths are changed by *refraction*.

CHAPTER TEN

Mirror and Lens Images

THE position, size and nature of any image formed by a lens or a spherical mirror can be determined by drawing a diagram to scale. This is not as accurate as methods based on mathematical calculation, but it is easier to understand.

It is only necessary to trace the paths of two rays in order to locate the image —the important thing is to choose, out of the countless rays spreading out from the object, the two which pass through certain fixed points. It is, of course, necessary to know something about the lens or mirror being used.

Spherical Mirrors

No matter how they are made, spherical mirrors can be regarded as parts of a hollow silvered glass ball. The *radius of curvature* (symbol r) of the mirror is simply the radius of the glass sphere of which it forms part. The *centre of curvature* (symbol C) is simply the centre of the sphere. A line drawn through the centre of curvature to hit the middle of the mirror is called the *axis*; the point at which it hits the mirror is called the *pole* (symbol P).

Half-way between the centre of curvature and the pole is a point called the *principal focus* (symbol F).

All rays of light travelling parallel to the axis of a concave mirror are reflected back through the principal focus. If rays of light travelling parallel to the axis fall on a convex mirror they spread out after reflection; the principal focus in this case is the point from which they *appear* to be spreading. The distance from the focus to the pole is called the *focal length* (symbol f). Any ray which travels parallel to the axis of a concave mirror will be reflected through the focus. (Any ray travelling parallel to the axis of a convex mirror will be reflected away from the focus.)

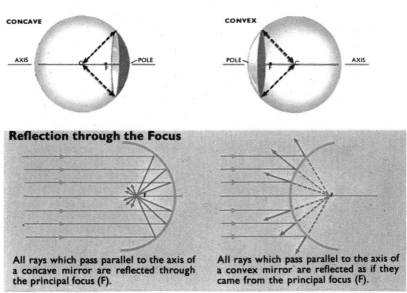

CONCAVE

AXIS
C · F
POLE

CONVEX

POLE
F · C
AXIS

Reflection through the Focus

All rays which pass parallel to the axis of a concave mirror are reflected through the principal focus (F).

All rays which pass parallel to the axis of a convex mirror are reflected as if they came from the principal focus (F).

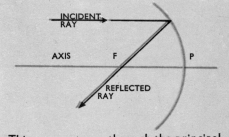

This ray must pass through the principal focus (F) after reflection.

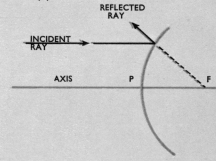

This ray must appear to come from the principal focus (F) after reflection.

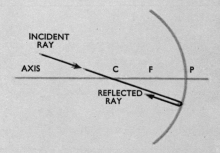

Any ray passing through the centre of curvature (C) must hit the mirror at 90° and will be reflected back along its own path.

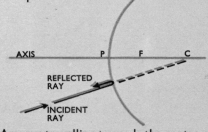

Any ray travelling towards the centre of curvature (C) must hit the mirror at 90° and will be reflected back along its own path.

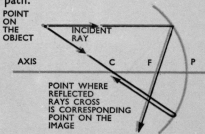

These are two rays whose paths can be predicted. Where they cross after reflection is a point on the image.

Any ray passing through the centre of curvature must hit the surface of a concave mirror at right-angles (this is simple geometry) and according to the laws of reflection it will be reflected back along its own path. Any ray travelling towards the centre of curvature of a convex mirror will hit the reflecting surface at right-angles and will return along its own path.

With these facts in mind it should be possible to draw two rays from any point on the object. One ray is drawn parallel to the axis; the other ray is drawn through the centre of curvature. For simplicity the rays are always drawn from the top of the object. The point where they meet after reflection is the top of the image. If they do not meet they must be traced back to an imaginary point from which they appear to come. If the object is arranged vertically with its base on the axis the base of the image will also lie on the axis. Once the top of the image has been located the whole image can simply be sketched in vertically between the axis and point representing the top of the image.

Lenses

The *axis* of a lens is the line which passes through the middle of the lens at right angles to its surfaces. Rays of light travelling parallel to the axis of a converging lens are gathered up so that they all pass through a point called the principal focus (symbol F). (The principal focus of a diverging lens is the point from which rays travelling parallel to the axis *appear* to come after the lens has spread them out.) Any ray which travels parallel to the axis of a converging lens will, after being refracted,

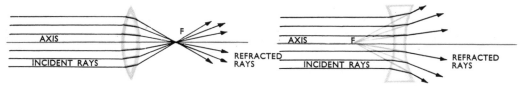

All rays which lie parallel to the axis of a converging lens are refracted through the principal focus (F).

All rays which lie parallel to the axis of a diverging lens are refracted so that they appear to come from the principal focus (F).

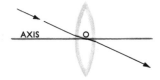

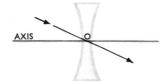

A ray passing through the optical centre (O) of a converging lens is not deviated from its original direction.

A ray passing through the optical centre (O) of a diverging lens is not deviated from its original direction.

pass through the principal focus. (Any ray which travels parallel to the axis of a diverging lens will, after refraction *appear* to be travelling away from the principal focus.) The distance from the principal focus to the mid-point of the lens is called the focal length (symbol f).

Any ray passing through the mid-point of a lens (called the optical centre, symbol O, not to be confused with centre of curvature) will carry on without being deviated from its original path. It may be refracted (bent) as it enters the lens, but the bending is cancelled out as it leaves the other side of the lens.

To find the position of the image formed by a lens it is only necessary to draw two rays spreading out from

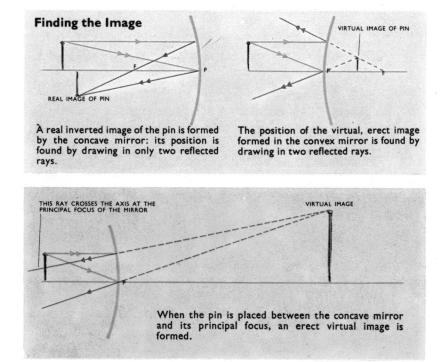

Finding the Image

A real inverted image of the pin is formed by the concave mirror: its position is found by drawing in only two reflected rays.

The position of the virtual, erect image formed in the convex mirror is found by drawing in two reflected rays.

When the pin is placed between the concave mirror and its principal focus, an erect virtual image is formed.

the topmost point of the object. One is drawn straight through the optical centre of the lens. The other is drawn parallel to the axis and, on emerging from the lens, passes through the principal focus. (In the case of a diverging lens this ray will appear to be travelling away from the principal focus.) The point where the two rays meet (even if they have to be traced back to an imaginary meeting point) is the top of the image. If the object is vertical with its base on the axis, the image will also be vertical with its base on the axis. Having located

the top of the image the rest of it can be sketched in between this point and the axis.

Ray diagrams for both mirrors and lenses are easier to draw (and actually give better results) if the bending (reflection or refraction) is shown taking place on an imaginary line drawn at right-angles to the axis through the pole or optical centre. In fact it is not necessary to draw in the lens or mirror at all once this construction line has been inserted.

FINDING THE IMAGE – REAL IMAGES

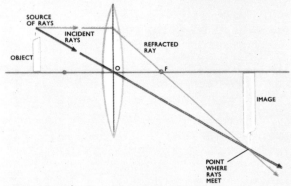

This object is slightly more than the focal length away from a converging lens. The image is formed at a considerable distance from the lens. It is inverted and magnified. Because it is produced by the meeting of actual light rays it is a real image.

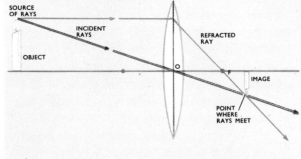

This object is over twice the focal length away from a converging lens. The image is formed just beyond the focus. It is inverted and diminished. Because it is produced by the meeting of actual light rays it is a real image.

FINDING THE IMAGE – VIRTUAL IMAGES

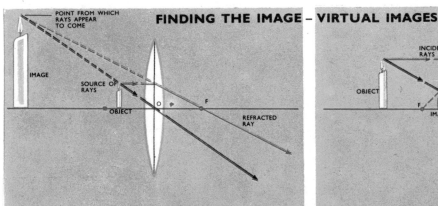

This object is less than the focal length away from a converging lens. The image is formed on the same side of the lens. It is upright and magnified. It is a virtual image since light rays only appear to come from it.

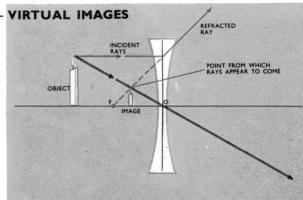

This object could be anywhere in front of a diverging lens. The image is formed on the same side of the lens. It is upright and diminished. It is a virtual image since light rays only appear to come from it.

CHAPTER ELEVEN

Finding the Focal Length

THE designer of an optical instrument needs to know the focal lengths of the lenses or mirrors he is using. When he has this information, he can work out the positions of the various components of the system to give the required magnification and to bring the image to focus in the correct position.

The focal length of a lens or mirror will determine, to some extent, the purpose for which it can be used. For instance, a convex lens (thicker at the centre than at the edge) of short focal length is ideal for use as a magnifying glass (simple microscope) whereas a convex lens of long focal length is necessary in a camera if large images of distant objects are required.

As the focal length is such an important property of the lens or mirror, various methods have been devised for measuring the distance. The methods described here give a value of the focal length by direct measurement: no calculation is necessary in arriving at the result. How-

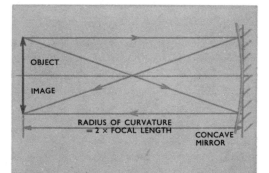

Concave Mirror

If rays of light travelling parallel to its principal axis strike a concave mirror they are reflected through the focus of the mirror. Conversely rays passing through the focus of this type of mirror are reflected so that they are parallel to its principal axis. If an object is set up at the centre of curvature of a concave mirror, some rays from it will reach the mirror by travelling parallel to the principal axis while others will pass through the focus. A real and inverted image of the object is formed at the centre of curvature.

This suggests an easy way of finding the focal length of a concave mirror since the centre of curvature is twice as far from the mirror as the focus. A pin is slowly moved towards the mirror. At first it produces an image which is smaller than the object and closer to the mirror. But gradually the image gets bigger at the same time moving away from the mirror. Eventually a point is reached when object and image are the same size and are in the same plane. This can be checked for no parallax – both pins appear to move as one. The distance of the pin from the mirror is measured – half this distance is the focal length of the mirror.

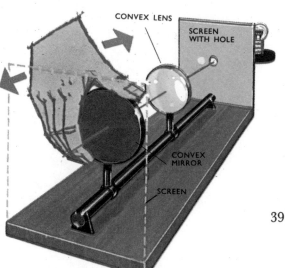

Finding the focal length of a convex mirror. The mirror is moved backwards and forwards until a sharp image of the light source appears on the screen with the hole in it.

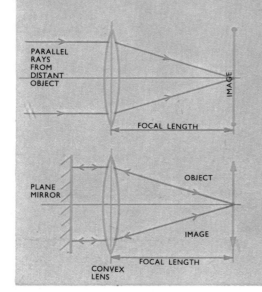

Convex Lens

When rays of light from a distant object pass through a convex lens (thicker at the centre than at the edge) they form an image in the focal plane of the lens. This is because these rays are almost parallel to one another and rays parallel to the principal axis of a convex lens converge on the focus. This is used in a very quick (but approximate) method of finding the focal length

The lens is used to produce a sharp image of a distant object on a screen. (A sheet of plane paper pinned on a drawing board will serve quite well as a screen.) It is often satisfactory to produce an image of the window frame or of building visible through the window. By directing the light on to

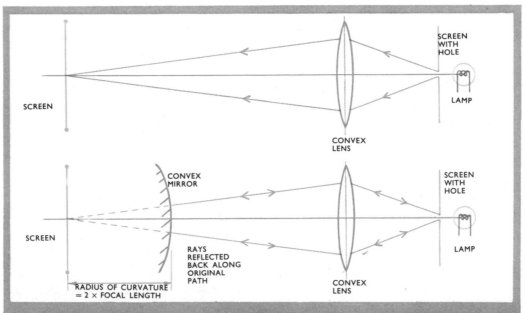

Convex Mirror

Rays of light directed at the centre of curvature of a convex mirror strike its surface at right angles and are reflected back along the same path.

In this method of finding the focal length of a convex mirror, a *convex lens* is first set up in front of a white screen. A screen with a hole in it is placed in front of the lens and a light is placed behind the small hole in the screen. The lens is then moved backwards and forwards until there is a sharp image of the illuminated hole on the screen. These parts of the system must now remain in these positions.

Then the convex mirror is placed between the screen and the lens. The mirror is moved backwards and forwards until a sharp image of the illuminated hole appears on the screen with the hole in it. The mirror must be reflecting light back along its original path, so the centre of curvature of the mirror is at the point on the screen where the first sharp image was formed. The distance between the mirror and screen is measured and the focal length of the mirror is half this distance.

the screen and moving the lens backwards and forwards, the position of the lens giving the sharpest image is found. The distance from the lens to the screen is the focal length.

In a somewhat better method based on the same principle, a plane mirror is placed behind the lens and is used to ensure that the rays parallel to the principal axis are truly parallel. A pin is used as the object and is moved towards the lens until an inverted image of the pin is formed head to head with the object pin. The method of parallax is used to confirm that the image and object are in the same plane. When this condition is achieved the distance of the object from the lens is the focal length.

Focus and Focal Length

Rays of light travelling parallel to the axis of a lens or mirror are bent when they pass through the lens or are reflected by the mirror. The point on which the rays converge (come together), or from which they appear to diverge (fan out) is called the *focus*. The distance from the focus to the lens or mirror is its *focal length*. Lenses and mirrors having short focal lengths are said to be more *powerful* than those with longer focal lengths.

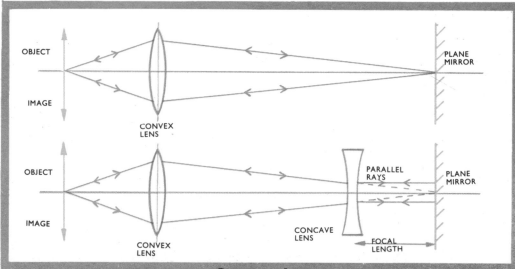

Concave Lens

If light travelling parallel to the principal axis of a concave lens (thicker at the edge than at the centre) strikes the lens it is made to diverge (fan out) as if it originated from the focus of the lens. Conversely a beam converging upon the focus of a concave lens emerges as a parallel beam.

In this method for finding the focal length of a concave lens, a *convex* lens is set up some distance in front of a plane mirror. A pin is then placed in front of the lens and is moved until the image created by the lens and plane mirror seems to coincide with the pin, i.e. there is no parallax. These parts of the system must now be left undisturbed.

Next the concave lens under examination is placed between the convex lens and the mirror. The *concave* lens is then moved until there is no parallax between the image of the pin and the pin. Then the distance of the concave lens from the mirror equals the focal length of the concave lens. It is only under these conditions that the rays from the object can form an image in the same plane. The rays which formerly converged upon the mirror must now be reflected at right angles by it.

ever, some of these methods yield only approximate values, while others giving greater accuracy entail quite a lot of calculation.

Locating the focus of convex lenses and concave mirrors is quite easy because both yield *real* images (i.e. images which can be formed on a screen) of real objects. In contrast, concave lenses and concave mirrors always produce *virtual* images of real objects. Virtual images are more difficult to find because light rays do not actually pass through them – they only appear to do so. A convex lens can be used to create a virtual object for the concave lens or convex mirror and this virtual object in turn yields a real image.

Several of the methods require the position of an object and its image to coincide. This can be checked by the *method of parallax*. Very briefly, this is done by the observer moving his head from side to side. If the object and image do not coincide, one will have moved further than the other. However, if they are in the same plane their positions will always coincide, irrespective of the position from which they are viewed.

CHAPTER TWELVE

Lens Combinations

OPTICAL systems – for example microscopes, telescopes and cameras – usually contain several lenses. When designing a combination of several lenses it is unnecessary to know the way light rays are bent (*refracted*) each time they enter or leave a lens. Whether the final image is large or small, real or virtual, situated at infinity or a fraction of an inch away from the eyepiece lens, the features of the final image can be found by a simple construction once a few simple facts about the lenses are known.

The properties of individual lenses and lens combinations can be found by experiment. Certain points associated with the lenses are called the *cardinal points*. These are important because each of the rays constructed in the ray diagram goes through at least one cardinal point. The cardinal points are called the *principal points*, the *principal foci* and the *nodal points*. In a lens combination they can be found by experiment, and also by calculation from the cardinal points of individual lenses.

The Principal Points and Planes

A single thin lens has one principal point and two principal foci. It is usual to represent the thin lens as a line – the *principal plane*. All the light-bending takes place at the principal plane, which cuts the optical axis of the lens at the *principal* point. Rays passing through the principal point are not bent.

All rays from the object which are parallel to the axis, pass through one of the *foci* after they have travelled through the lens. The two principal foci are on either side of the lens, one for rays approaching it from the left hand side and the other from the right hand side. To find the position of the image formed by a single thin lens, two rays only need be drawn in. One of these goes from the top of the object, parallel to the optical axis, and bends

The Nodal Points

If one side of the lens combination is in air, and the other in water or oil, the paths of some of the rays will change. Water, air and oil have different *refractive indices* – light rays are refracted as they pass from one to the other, so there will be an extra bending in the optical system. This would be an important consideration when designing an underwater camera, or an oil immersion microscope. It is incorrect to draw the ray arriving at one of the principal points emerging from the other at the same angle to the optical axis. The incoming ray at the first principal point is not parallel to the outgoing ray at the second principal point.

However, at two other points along the optical axis, the incoming and outgoing rays from the top of the object, to the top of the image, will be parallel. These points are called the *nodal points*. They can be calculated once the refractive indices of the substances on either side of the lenses are known. To construct the image position in such a lens system, all six cardinal points must be known. But when there is air on both sides of the lens system, there are only four important cardinal points. The two nodal points coincide with the two principal points.

is one – the image is exactly the same size as an object situated at one principal plane, and also on the same side of the optical axis as the object. For a single thin lens this can happen at only one point – at the lens itself. With two lenses there are two possible points which can be found by projecting an object into the system, and finding the point where the image is the same size, with a travelling microscope. Alternatively, the position of the principal points can be calculated from the focal lengths of the individual lenses, and from their distance apart.

The focal length of the combination can also be found by experiments (which are similar to methods used for single thin lenses). But it, too, can be calculated from the focal lengths of the constituents. A simple mathematical relationship exists between them.

When the principal points and principal foci have been found the

at the principal plane to go through one of the principal foci. The other ray is not deviated, because it goes from the top of the object through the principal point of the lens. The two rays intersect at a point, which marks the top of the image.

When there are two or more lenses in the system, or when the lens is thick instead of thin, there are two principal planes. But these are not necessarily in the same position as the lenses. The principal planes are in fact defined as the planes where the magnification

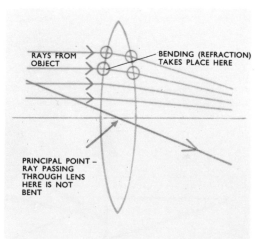

Light passing through a lens is actually bent at each surface. However, in simple ray diagrams it is possible to disregard this and draw all the bending at a single line (the principal plane) running down the centre of the lens.

43

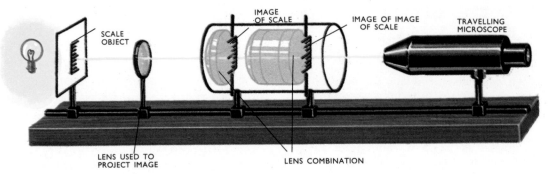

Finding the principal planes of a lens combination. These are the planes which give a magnification of one. The principal planes will probably occur in the middle of the system, where it is impossible to site an object. So the object, an illuminated scale, is projected into the combination. An image the same size is found with a travelling microscope.

position of any image can be found by drawing the path of two rays – the same two rays used for constructing the image in a single thin lens. The first of the two rays travel parallel to the optical axis until it meets the first of the two principal planes. What happens between the two principal planes is of no consequence. The ray must emerge from the second at exactly the same height above the optical axis. This follows from the

way the principal planes are defined. An object placed at one principal plane gives rise to an image at the **other principal plane, of the same size and on the same side of the axis.**

On emerging from the second principal plane, the constructed ray is bent so that it passes through one of the foci.

The second constructed ray is the one which does not change direction as it passes through the system. It is

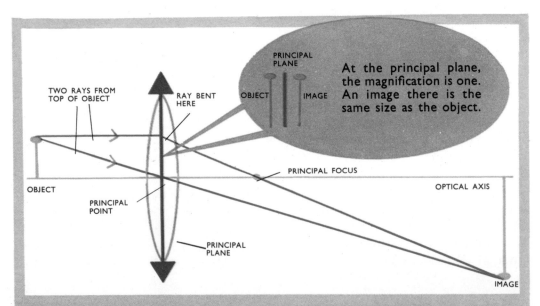

The position of the image can be found using a ray diagram. A thin lens is represented by a line, the *principal plane*. Of the infinite number of possible rays passing through the lens, only two are necessary to locate the top of the final image. One is bent: the other is not.

drawn from the top of the object, through to the first principal point. This ray makes a certain angle with the optical axis. Again, it does not matter what happens between the two principal planes. Another of their properties is that a ray arriving at one principal point travels away from the other along a path making the same angle with the optical axis. The incoming ray and the outgoing ray are therefore parallel to each other.

Together these two rays define the position of the top of the final image.

This simple theory of lenses works only for rays bunched closely around the centre of the lenses (called the *paraxial* region). Only images in this region are geometrically perfect. A small straight line object in the paraxial region is converted into a small straight line image by the simple lens, in the paraxial region. A larger straight line object straying out of the paraxial region would probably give rise to a curved image. The object must also be at right angles to the axis of the lens system for the simple lens theory to work. The image formation is different when the object is parallel to the axis.

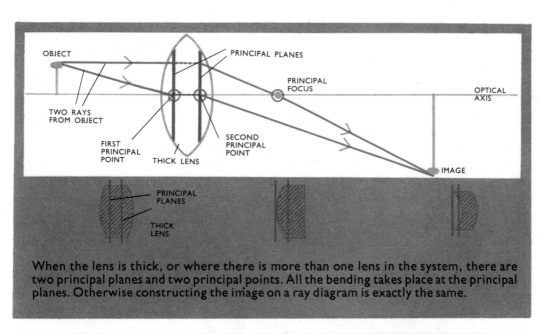

When the lens is thick, or where there is more than one lens in the system, there are two principal planes and two principal points. All the bending takes place at the principal planes. Otherwise constructing the image on a ray diagram is exactly the same.

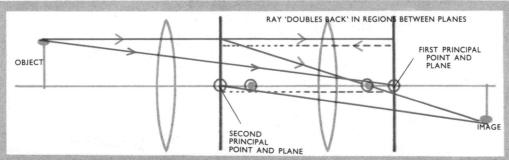

Ray tracing for a combination of two thin lenses. When these are separated by air, the positions of the principal planes are reversed. The one on the right is the first principal plane: the one on the left is the second. Doubling back is needed to draw in the rays. What happens to the rays between the principal planes is immaterial in this construction. An object placed at the first principal plane would give rise to an image the same side of the optical axis, and the same size as the object. This is the way principal planes are defined.

CHAPTER THIRTEEN

The Optical Bench

EXPERIMENTS with lenses and mirrors in optics usually involve finding the focal lengths of lenses and mirrors, measuring distances between objects, images and lenses, or finding the size of the magnified image produced by the lens system. Light rays do not bend as they pass from one stage to the next. They travel in straight lines. So the lenses, mirrors and screens used for the experiment are usually arranged in an absolutely straight line.

It is difficult to do this without some form of guide. The optical bench is simply a straight-line guide along which all the components can be moved until they are in the correct position – in line. Because distances between the optical components must be measured accurately, the bench has a built-in measuring scale, marked in millimetres. It can be anything over a metre long.

The lenses and mirrors are mounted on holders, which fit on to the bench. In some benches, the base of the holder is just a rectangular block of

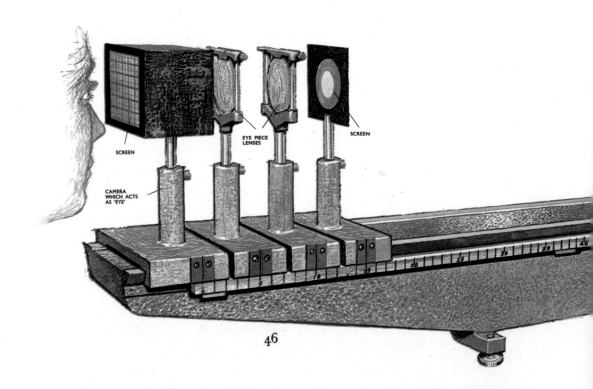

SCREEN

EYE PIECE
LENSES

SCREEN

CAMERA
WHICH ACTS
AS 'EYE'

wood, which moves along the metre scale. In more refined systems, the lens holders are made of metal, and can be clamped to the bench. A pointer on their base marks the exact position on the metre rule of the centre of the component.

Setting up an optical bench

The holders may be able to hold a variety of different components. Since it is likely that these will vary in size, the height of each holder is adjustable. The *optical height* of the system is the height to the optical centre of each of the components. This should be the same for all components. The holder for the lamp used as a light source is adjusted first, so that its height is convenient. Then all the other holders are adjusted until, on looking along the bench, the centres of the components appear to be on the same horizontal line.

Optical experiments are best done in a darkened room, so that the only light passing through the lens system comes from the lamp at one end of the bench. The amount of light coming from the lamp is adjusted by a dia-phragm, or *stop*. The size of a stop just in front of the lamp governs the amount of light passing through the whole optical system – in other words, it determines the brightness of the final image. Stops further along the optical bench may have additional effects on the image. The size of the stop allowing light to enter a camera (the *aperture*) affects both the bright-ness and the sharpness of the image.

Lenses and 'stops' are arranged on the optical bench to demonstrate the lens system of a compound microscope. A field *stop limits light from the lamp at the right hand end of the bench. Another stop, the* aperture *stop, limits the light further along the bench. This stop affects the sharpness of the final image. The object is a transparent scale, and the image is viewed through a camera, which acts like a human eye.*

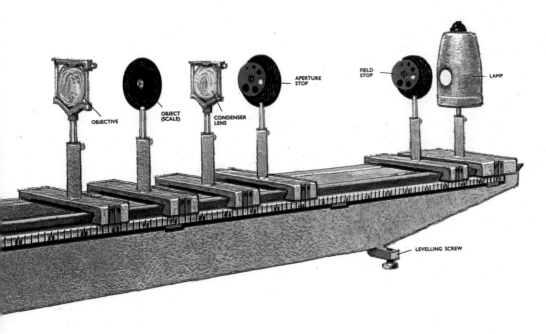

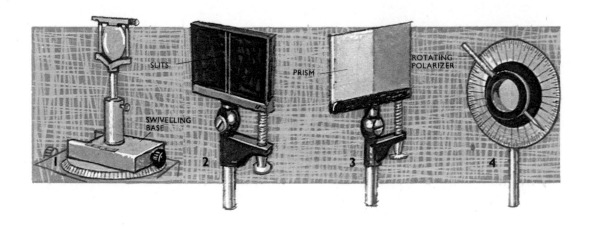

Components for optical benches. 1. *A swivelling holder for a lens.* 2. *Two fine slits are ruled on this coated glass plate. It is used in experiments on* interference *of light waves. When the slits are illuminated, a pattern of dark and light lines (interference fringes) can be produced on a screen.* 3. *This is a prism with one very large angle and two very small ones. It is called Fresnel's Biprism, and is also used to form fringe patterns in light interference experiments.* 4. *A polarizer. Light consists of vibrations both from side to side and up and down. The polarizer removes one of these two components.* 5. *A pointer is used to locate images. If the image coincides with the object, they should* always *coincide, no matter from which direction they are viewed. This is called the method of no parallax.* 6. *Slits are often used as objects.*

Effects like these can be investigated by setting up the optical system on an optical bench, altering the size of the stops, and watching the change in the appearance of the image.

If the magnification of the optical system is being measured, the 'object' should be something which can be sharply focused on a screen and easily measured. A small transparent millimetre scale makes a convenient object. The magnification can then be easily found by measuring the lengths of the scale divisions on the final image. Other convenient objects used are pin-hole size openings in a black plate. These isolate single 'pencils' of light rays travelling through the lenses, and are useful for studying the defects (or *aberrations*) of lenses.

All the components on an optical bench should be aligned initially. In fact, modified optical benches are used to align optical instruments, like binoculars and microscopes. Once an optical system has been aligned, the consequences of disaligning it can be studied on the optical bench.

Lenses and their Defects

CHAPTER FOURTEEN

The Eye and its Defects

NEAR the front of the eye is a lens through which rays of light are directed and focused so that an image falls on the retina at the back of the eye. (Most of the bending of the light is done by the cornea at the front of the eye.) The retina picks up the rays as a picture, and translates the image appearing on it into a message which is sent by the optic nerve to the brain. The brain interprets these signals as the picture we see.

Many of the defects which can occur in the eye are the result of inadequacies of the lens. The purpose of the lens is to refract or bend light rays on to the retina so that they arrive there as a sharp image.

Do you suffer from astigmatism? *Shut one eye and look at this picture. If all the lines appear equally dark you do not. But if some sets of lines appear dark and those at right-angles to them appear lighter, then you do. This is caused by the fact that the front of your eye or the lens surface is not all of the same curvature. One curved surface will focus light at one point whereas a different-sized curve will give a focus somewhere else.*

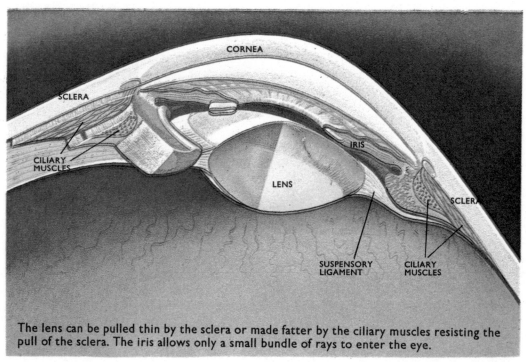

The lens can be pulled thin by the sclera or made fatter by the ciliary muscles resisting the pull of the sclera. The iris allows only a small bundle of rays to enter the eye.

Blind Spot
This is a part of the back of the eye with no nerve endings to pick up information about a picture focused on it. It is the area where the optic nerve leaves the eye. Hold the page up so that the dot and the cross are about two feet away from your eyes. Shut your right eye and look at the cross with your left eye. As you do so very slowly bring the paper towards your eyes. Although you are looking at the cross you can still see the dot. Then at a certain point the dot seems to disappear. It is then focused on the blind spot. As the page is moved forward it reappears.

The lens is capable of changing its shape so that the images of both near and distant objects can be focused clearly on the retina. The lens is composed of an arrangement of lens fibres inside an elastic lens capsule. The fibres are arranged in such a way that when the eye is in strain, doing close work, the lens is fat and when the eye is relaxed, looking into the distance, the lens is thinner. When the eye is relaxed, the elastic force of the sclera (white skin which is seen at the front of the eye and which encloses the whole of the eyeball) pulls the lens thin by pulling on the suspensory ligament attached to the lens. To make the lens fatter, the ciliary muscle resists the elastic force of the sclera. There is less pull on the lens which becomes fatter.

Short- and Long-sightedness

For an object close to the eye the lens must become fatter to focus properly. This property of the eye which makes it able to adjust itself is called *accommodation*. After much close work has been done, the eye seems to think that close work is what is required of it always and alters itself permanently to make the task easier. The difficulty then comes if distance viewing is required. The lens cannot accommodate itself by making itself thin enough to focus the distant object without strain, and spectacles are needed. Without spectacles the eye would try to focus the distant object as though it were

Are your glasses corrected for astigmatism? *Hold them horizontally about two feet away from your eyes and look at the corner angle of a doorway or window, then tilt the glasses. If the corner appears to tilt, too, then the glasses are corrected for astigmatism.*

much nearer and the result would be a blurred image on the retina. A concave lens of the correct shape will spread out the light rays, making them seem to come from a nearer object so that the eye can obtain a clear image. The correct term for short sight is *myopia*.

Long sight can be caused by the eyeball being too short from front to back or by the hardening of the lens. A long-sighted eye can be one which is too short and because of its shape can focus distant objects, but not those close to. Converging lenses are worn to bring together the light rays so that a clear image can be obtained on the retina. The correct word for this type of long sight is *hypermetropia*.

Presbyopia is the name given to the eye complaint of old age. As you grow older the lens hardens and becomes less pliable so that the eye muscles have not the power in them to make the lens of the eye round and fat enough to focus objects which are close to it. Special reading glasses are needed, similar to the ones used by long-sighted people. These glasses are of no use for distance viewing, so the person must take them off and wear another pair or have bifocal spectacles which have two sets of lenses, the bottom set for close work and the upper for distance viewing.

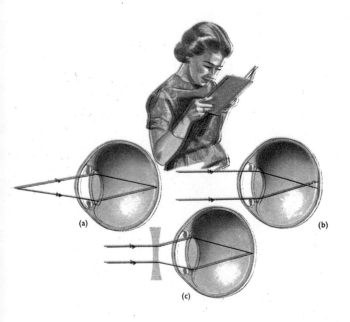

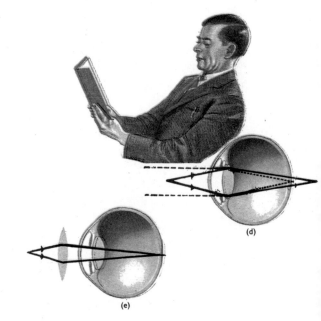

Short sight.
(a) *A near object can give a clear image.*
(b) *For distance viewing the short-sighted eye gives a blurred image as the light is brought into focus before the retina.*
(c) *A diverging lens is used to correct this.*

Long sight.
(d) *For a near object the long-sighted eye focuses the light behind the retina, giving a blurred image.*
(e) *A converging lens corrects this defect.*

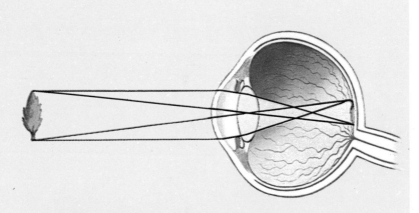

Ray diagram showing how the normal eye focuses a sharp image on the retina. The eye is kept in shape by the liquid inside it. Light rays entering the eye are bent at the corneal surface and further gathered up by the lens.

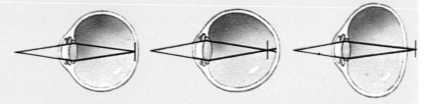

Eye defects can be due to distortion of the eyeball. The short-sighted eyeball (*centre*) is too long and the long-sighted eyeball (*right*) is too short.

CHAPTER FIFTEEN

The Manufacture of Lenses

IN an optical system every lens is made to do a particular job and the light passing through it must follow a predesigned path. This means that the lenses must be made with their surfaces accurately ground to particular curvatures and the glass must be of such a composition that the correct amount of bending takes place when the light rays enter and leave. The *refractive index* of glass, which determines the amount the light bends in the lens, varies with the composition of the glass.

First of all, optical glass of high quality must be made. Its composition is accurately controlled so that the glass is of the required standard. For example, the glass may contain *stabi-*

lizers which prevent it from blackening on exposure to gamma rays. Most spectacle lenses are made of colourless glass known in the trade as *white glass* but about 15% are tinted to give protection against glare.

The raw materials, which are usually a mixture of sand, sodium carbonate or sulphate, and calcium carbonate are heated electrically in platinum lined pots and well stirred to make certain the composition is the same throughout. There are several ways of dealing with the molten glass, to make it into small slabs or *blanks* from which lenses can be ground.

In the oldest method the glass is allowed to cool down slowly and solidify in the pot. The pot is then

A stirring machine mixes the molten glass in the furnace.

Pot of molten optical glass being emptied.

shattered so that the glass can be removed. On removal it is reheated until just molten and then pressed into slabs which are polished on both sides so that they can be examined for defects such as air bubbles. About half the slabs are returned to the melting pot because they are defective.

Alternatively, the molten glass can be passed through rollers to form a sheet which is cut into pieces of suitable size. These pieces are re-heated in a furnace and then pressed in dies to make them approximately the shape of the lens.

In the latest method a hot sluggish stream of glass is drawn continuously from the pot and cut automatically into pieces of a predetermined weight. These hot pieces of glass drop into one of a number of moulds on a continuously turning table. A top plunger then presses the hot glass into the approximate shape of the lens. The roughly shaped lens is known as a *blank*.

Whichever way the blank has been made it contains internal stresses and strains caused by cooling too quickly. These are points of weakness in the glass which make it liable to break and crack. They are dealt with by *annealing* in an *annealing lehr* (an enclosed oven). Here, the blanks are heated and allowed to cool down very slowly indeed to get rid of internal stresses.

The blanks must then be ground to make them into lenses. Here, a very high accuracy is required, for the lens must often be correctly cut to within 2 millionths of an inch. This grinding is done in several stages.

Diamond grinding machines are used to quickly grind the blanks to the required thickness and curvature. The diamond grinding machine consists of a lower rotating spindle to which the glass blank can be fitted. Above it is another rotating spindle which carries a tubular diamond tool. The spindle which carries the diamond tool can move from side to side. If the upper and lower spindles are in line with each other (i.e. their axes are parallel) then

A glass moulding machine pressing blobs of molten glass into approximate lens shapes.

the top surface of the blank is ground flat. The upper spindle is tilted to produce curved surfaces. If the axes of the two spindles intersect above the glass surface then a concave surface is ground, but if they intersect below, the surface will be convex. Softer grinding tools would be quickly worn down and the spindle would consequently need frequent adjustment, but because diamonds are so hard, up to 250,000 spectacle lenses can be accurately ground with one tool at one setting. During grinding, friction between the tool and the lens would cause overheating. A constant flow of a solution of a soluble oil in water keeps the lens cool.

It is usual to grind, smooth and polish the convex side of the lens first and then deal similarly with the other side after the first side has been completed.

For the lenses to be *smoothed* and *polished* it is important that they are held so that they cannot slip. It is also a help if several lenses can be treated at one time. Spectacle lenses are generally dealt with in lots of 3 to 7. The roughly ground lenses are heated to about 70–80°C and placed ground side down in a mould. The curvature of the mould is the same as that of the

Blocking press. Lenses are mounted in blocks for smoothing and polishing.

Block of lenses placed on polishing machine.

lens surfaces. A hot pad of semi-molten blocking material is pressed firmly into position in the mould so that the lenses become embedded in it. The *blocking compound* cools and sets. When it has set, the block is removed from the mould. At one time, pitch was used as a blocking compound but it has now been replaced by synthetic compounds which do not disease the skins of the workers handling them.

The blocks of lenses then go to a *lapping* machine for *smoothing*. Here, large scratches are smoothed away. If the concave sides of the lenses are being smoothed, then the cast iron smoothing tool has the same curvature, only it is convex, and vice versa. The convex (bulging) component is fixed to a vertical rotating spindle. The concave component is fixed above it on the end of a pivoted arm so that it can move horizontally, vertically, and rotate while it is doing so. A slurry of aluminium oxide abrasive is fed between the two rotating parts. The

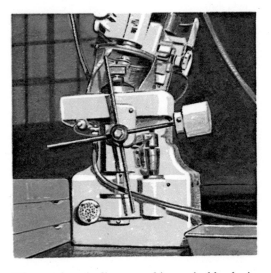

Diamond grinding machine. A blank is being roughly ground to the required thickness and curvature.

smoothing process takes from 15 to 30 minutes to complete. A trough underneath prevents the slurry from splashing out.

After smoothing, the blocks are washed free of slurry and the lenses are checked to see that they are of the correct curvature.

The final polishing is carried out on a similar machine, only this time the polishing tool is covered with a hard pad of felt and cerium oxide. Zirconium oxide slurry may also be used as a polishing compound.

After polishing, the lenses are examined to check that their surfaces are perfect. They are then removed from the blocks. This is done by cooling the blocks. The blocking compound shrinks much more than the lenses. The lenses loosen so that they can be easily removed. They are then passed back to the beginning of the line so that the other side can be dealt with.

Inspecting finished surfaces for flaws.

CHAPTER SIXTEEN

The Blooming of Lenses

WHEN a camera lens is held up to the light and moved around so that the reflections from its surfaces can be seen, the lens appears to have a dull purple colour. Glints of purplish blue light come off, making it resemble the surface of a blue plum. The lens has been *bloomed*. A thin layer of *magnesium fluoride* has been deposited on its surfaces.

The lens has not become a piece of purple stained glass. Everything looks purple through purple stained glass because it transmits only purple light. All colours can be viewed through a bloomed lens. A green blade of grass will appear green and a blue sky will appear blue. The surface of a bloomed lens certainly reflects some purple light, but the lens will allow all the colours of the spectrum to pass through it.

Lenses are bloomed to make the image brighter and to give better contrast. The coating on the lens allows more light to pass through and decreases the amount of light reflected by the lens surfaces. Field glasses with no blooming give a dull, somewhat flat picture. The coating on the lenses, instead of giving a duller picture, makes it more vivid, and by reducing the stray reflections improves the contrast.

Blooming has now become common practice on all camera lenses and lenses in binoculars. It was first used after it was noticed that binoculars improved as their lenses grew old and were stained by impurities in the air.

Why does blooming work?

The layer of magnesium fluoride deposited on the surface is carefully adjusted to be $\frac{1}{4}$ of a wavelength of light thick. Light can have a series of different wavelengths. Red light has the longest wavelength and violet light, at the other end of the spectrum, has the shortest. The thickness of the layer is chosen to correspond to $\frac{1}{4}$ a wavelength of yellow light because yellow is in the middle of the spectrum and therefore is the most representative.

Without blooming, a lens surface may reflect 5% of the light falling on it and transmit the rest. The 5% is scattered and lost. More light is also lost by reflection at the second surface of the lens.

When light hits the upper layer of

The lenses and bell jar are cleaned by the passage of an electric discharge before blooming.

ELECTRODES

FILAMENT

MAGNESIUM FLUORIDE

VACUUM

Blooming lenses. In a vacuum some magnesium fluoride evaporates off from a molten pellet and deposits itself on the bell jar and the undersides of the lenses. Blooming is stopped by letting in air when the layer is thick enough. The person operating the unit can tell when the layer is thick enough because he gets a purple reflection from the lenses.

59

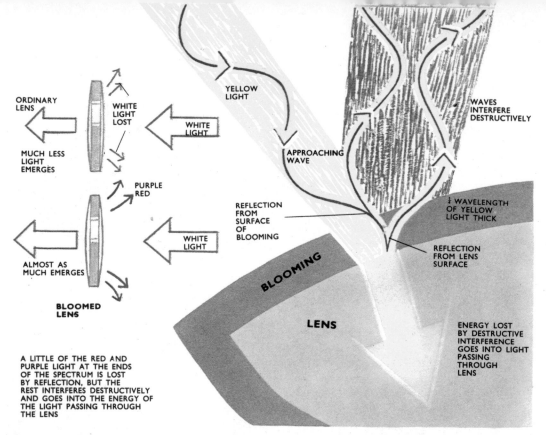

ORDINARY
LENS

WHITE
LIGHT
LOST

WHITE
LIGHT

MUCH LESS
LIGHT
EMERGES

PURPLE
RED

WHITE
LIGHT

ALMOST AS
MUCH EMERGES

BLOOMED
LENS

A LITTLE OF THE RED AND
PURPLE LIGHT AT THE ENDS
OF THE SPECTRUM IS LOST
BY REFLECTION, BUT THE
REST INTERFERES DESTRUCTIVELY
AND GOES INTO THE ENERGY OF
THE LIGHT PASSING THROUGH
THE LENS

YELLOW
LIGHT

WAVES
INTERFERE
DESTRUCTIVELY

APPROACHING
WAVE

REFLECTION
FROM
SURFACE
OF
BLOOMING

$\frac{1}{4}$ WAVELENGTH
OF YELLOW
LIGHT THICK

REFLECTION
FROM LENS
SURFACE

BLOOMING

LENS

ENERGY LOST
BY DESTRUCTIVE
INTERFERENCE
GOES INTO LIGHT
PASSING
THROUGH
LENS

The blooming consists of a layer of magnesium fluoride $\frac{1}{4}$ of a wavelength of yellow light thick. Reflections from the top and under surfaces of the layer interfere and destroy each other. The energy goes into the light passing through the lens.

the blooming, some is reflected but most passes through. Again, at the underside of the magnesium fluoride most of the light passes on into the lens, but some is reflected back. When this light reflected from the lower surface emerges from the fluoride, it has travelled exactly $\frac{1}{2}$ wavelength of yellow light more than the light reflected by the top surface. The two lots of reflected light are exactly out of phase with one another. A crest of one wave coincides with a trough of the other. The waves *interfere* and *destroy* each other. Therefore the amount of reflected light is greatly diminished. Although the waves have destroyed one another, their energy cannot be lost. It goes into the light passing through the lens. Instead of being reflected away at the surface, most of the light now passes through.

This system was designed to work well for the middle of the spectrum. It does not work very well for the colours at the ends. Some red, blue and purple light is lost by reflection. It is this light coming off that gives the lens its purplish bloom.

In some special lenses there may be two or three layers of blooming to cut down on the purple and red light lost by reflection. The thicknesses are arranged to cause destructive interference with the purple and red light.

An ordinary magnifying glass would never be bloomed. It has only two reflecting surfaces so little light would be lost. Also both surfaces are exposed and the blooming could be rubbed off if the owner of the lens is very fond of buffing and cleaning it.

Blooming is generally done where there is a whole system of lenses and many surfaces where light could be lost by reflection. A pair of binoculars has perhaps 14 lenses and 4 prisms, making 36 surfaces in all where light could be lost by reflection. Without blooming, perhaps over a half of the light is lost. With blooming, it may be less than 10%.

Many manufacturers bloom only the inner surfaces that are protected from grit, dust and people with dusters. The outer ones, they leave.

Blooming a lens

Only freshly ground, optically accurate lenses are suitable for blooming. There is no point in blooming old lenses because they will have become scratched in use and will have to be re-polished.

Before the lenses can be bloomed, they have to be absolutely clean. They are cleaned by dipping them in ethyl alcohol, and then mounted in a jig. The jigs used here are triangular sheets of metal with holes of the correct size to take the lenses.

The magnesium fluoride is coated on the lenses by *vacuum deposition*. In a vacuum, magnesium fluoride evapor-

ates off a molten pellet and deposits itself on the facing side of the lens.

The jigs are arranged in a bell jar over a metal boat containing the fluoride pellet. Two pumps begin to evacuate the air. When most of the air has been removed and the pressure is only 0·0008 mm of mercury, the bell jar and lenses are further cleaned by an *electric discharge*. An arc is struck between two metal electrodes. The ions that bound and rebound off the inner surfaces bombard away any remaining dirt. As pumping continues, the discharge weakens until it finally stops.

A current flows through the boat containing the fluoride and electrically heats it. The pellet melts and then starts to evaporate, depositing itself evenly over the inside of the bell jar and the lenses. An electric light is held over the lenses and the reflection of the filament from them is watched. As the layer of fluoride grows thicker, the colour of the reflection changes from yellow to yellow-mauve to mauve. When it is mauve, the layer is thick enough. Air is then let into the bell jar.

Blooming cuts down on the light lost by reflection at a glass surface. Consequently objects viewed through the bloomed glass are much brighter.

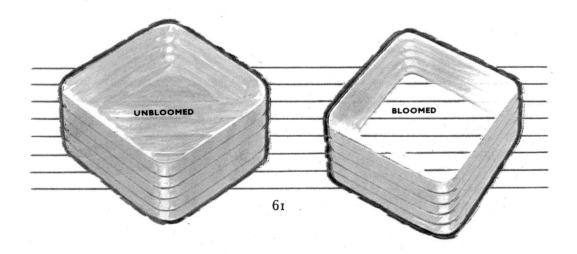

CHAPTER SEVENTEEN

Defects of Lenses

THE most serious defect interfering with the proper working of a lens is called *chromatic aberration*. If light were all of one type chromatic (colour) aberration would not arise. But white light is a mixture of all the colours in the rainbow, which when they pass through a lens all become individualists, taking slightly different routes. This is because the bending (refraction) is caused by the slowing down of the light as it enters the glass, and this in turn depends upon the wavelength (distance from crest to crest measured along the wave) of the light. Red light has a longer wavelength than light of any other colour and is bent *less* than light of any other colour. Red rays passing through a

simple convex lens come to a focus slightly farther from the lens than the focus of the violet rays. Rays of other colours come to foci in between. The lens has many foci instead of just one, and instead of just one sharp image it forms a series of overlapping images of different colours.

Lenses used in optical instruments such as telescopes and cameras have to be corrected for chromatic aberration. A corrected lens is called an *achromat*. A typical achromat is made by combining a convex crown glass lens with a weaker concave flint glass lens. Crown glass contains lime and potash, flint glass contains lead and potash. The two components are glued together with a transparent

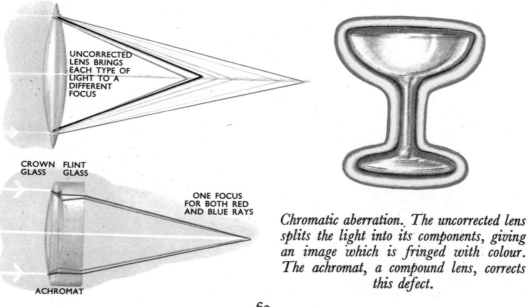

UNCORRECTED LENS BRINGS EACH TYPE OF LIGHT TO A DIFFERENT FOCUS

CROWN GLASS FLINT GLASS

ONE FOCUS FOR BOTH RED AND BLUE RAYS

ACHROMAT

Chromatic aberration. The uncorrected lens splits the light into its components, giving an image which is fringed with colour. The achromat, a compound lens, corrects this defect.

cement such as Canada balsam. The convex lens converges the light rays but disperses their colours; the concave lens, while spreading the light slightly, recombines the colours so that the red rays and the blue rays follow the same path. A similar correction can be obtained by mounting two separate thin convex lenses a suitable distance apart.

Spherical aberration is due to rays passing through the edge of a lens coming to a different focus from rays passing through the centre. A lens suffering from this defect has a series of foci and forms a series of overlapping images instead of a sharp single image.

The easiest method of overcoming spherical aberration is to avoid using the outermost parts of the lens. Many of the lenses used in cameras are just the central portions of much larger lenses. Alternatively a *stop* may be placed in front or behind a lens to cut off the outer rays. A stop is a screen with a hole in its centre. In some cases the size of the stop is variable, like the pupil of the eye. Cutting out the rays which hit the edge of the lens does not alter the size of the image but it does make the

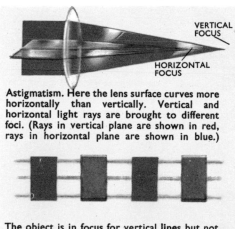

Astigmatism. Here the lens surface curves more horizontally than vertically. Vertical and horizontal light rays are brought to different foci. (Rays in vertical plane are shown in red, rays in horizontal plane are shown in blue.)

The object is in focus for vertical lines but not for horizontal ones.

image less bright. In cases where the brightness of the image is important spherical aberration has to be overcome without the use of a stop. The best method is to replace the single lens by two (or more) separate lenses so that the bending of light rays is shared in easy stages between them.

When the surfaces of a lens are curved more in one direction than another (i.e., they are not entirely spherical), a defect known as *astigmatism* arises. It frequently occurs in the lens of the eye where it can be corrected by the use of spectacles.

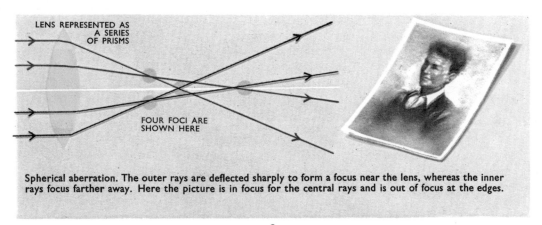

Spherical aberration. The outer rays are deflected sharply to form a focus near the lens, whereas the inner rays focus farther away. Here the picture is in focus for the central rays and is out of focus at the edges.

Mirror Adjustment

Light shining on the mirror is directed onto the object by adjusting the tilt of the mirror. If daylight is used, use light from a cloudy part of the sky, not sunshine direct.

Low-power Focusing

To focus the object under low power, rack the tube down until the objective almost touches the slide, using the coarse adjustment, then rack upwards until object is in focus.

High-power Focusing

Wind the body tube, with the high-power objective lens in position, right down so that it is almost touching the specimen, by rotating the coarse adjustment forwards.

Slowly move the coarse adjustment (large knob) backwards (towards you), so raising the high-power objective away from the specimen until it is in rough focus.

When the specimen is in rough focus rotate the fine adjustment (lower knob) until it is clearly in focus. The same procedure is carried out using the medium-power objective.

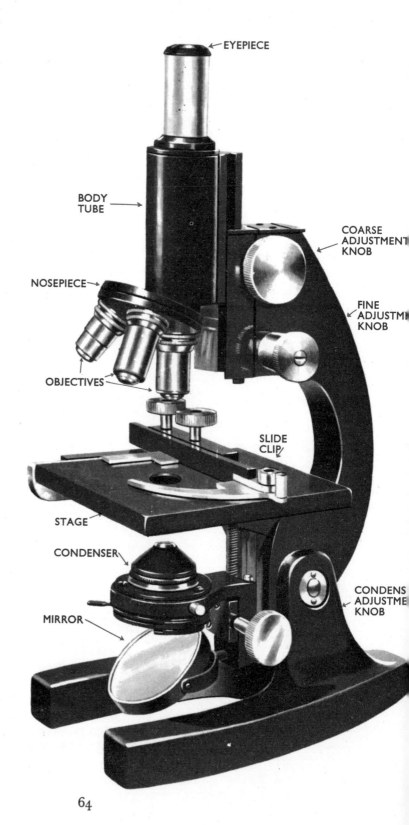

EYEPIECE

BODY TUBE

NOSEPIECE

OBJECTIVES

STAGE

CONDENSER

MIRROR

COARSE ADJUSTMENT KNOB

FINE ADJUSTM KNOB

SLIDE CLIP

CONDENS ADJUSTME KNOB

Optical Instruments

CHAPTER EIGHTEEN

Telescopes

THE telescope is used for magnifying distant objects. A lens or mirror called the *objective* supplies a small *real image* of the distant object. This image is smaller than the *object* itself. But a very much larger image is needed, so the small real image is magnified by another lens called the eyepiece. There are many different arrangements for achieving the same result.

There are two main types of optical telescope—the *refracting* telescope which has a lens as its objective to provide the small real image of the object. It is called the refracting telescope because the light rays are bent or refracted on passing through the objective lens. The other type is the *reflecting* telescope. Here, the objective is a mirror and because the light entering the telescope is reflected at the surface of the mirror it is called a reflecting telescope.

The ability of a telescope to show two objects that are close to each other as two separate images and not just as one image is called the resolv-

ing power of the telescope. It is obvious that a good telescope should have the largest possible resolving power. If the aperture (hole by which the light enters the telescope) is small, two stars which appear to be close to each other will appear to be only one star. To improve the resolving power and obtain two images, the aperture size must be increased. Incidentally good binoculars are expensive not because their magnification is higher than cheap ones but because they have wider objectives giving better resolution. It is difficult to make large lenses without stresses and strains inside them building up. Even then, when the lens is supported in position at the edges, it tends to sag under its own weight. Unlike a mirror, it cannot be supported underneath because this would prevent the light from passing through it. Yet another disadvantage of the refracting telescope is that light loses some energy in passing through the denser material that forms a lens whereas a mirror merely reflects

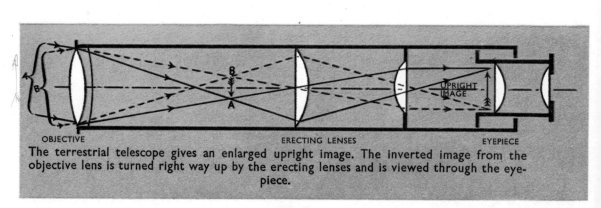

OBJECTIVE   ERECTING LENSES   EYEPIECE

The terrestrial telescope gives an enlarged upright image. The inverted image from the objective lens is turned right way up by the erecting lenses and is viewed through the eyepiece.

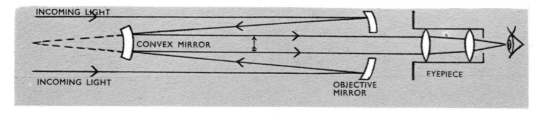

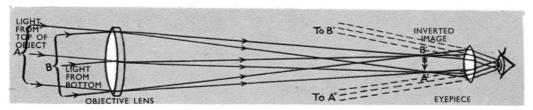

Cassegrain telescope. This is a reflecting telescope. The objective mirror has a hole in its centre to allow the light to pass to the eyepiece.

Refracting telescope (below). The eyepiece magnifies the small inverted image from the objective.

with less loss of energy.

An inverted image is useless for a *terrestrial* (land) *telescope*. The image must be the right way up. To do this, the telescope is designed with an erecting lens or system of lenses between the objective lens and eyepiece. This again makes the telescope longer and is the reason that the terrestrial refracting telescopes erected in various beauty spots and at the seaside are so enormously long.

It is obvious that this type of telescope is not portable. The ordinary portable pocket variety is the *Galilean telescope*, invented by Galileo over

three hundred years ago. The objective lens is still a biconvex lens which gathers up the light rays from the object so that they fall on a *biconcave* lens that acts as an eyepiece and provides an enlarged, virtual image which is nearer than the object.

The Astronomical Refracting Telescope

Light from a far distant source will, by the time it reaches the Earth, be in the form of rays of light which are parallel to each other. The rays from the 'top' of the star will be

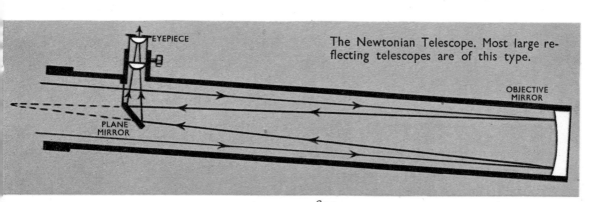

The Newtonian Telescope. Most large reflecting telescopes are of this type.

parallel and so will those from the 'bottom'. When some of these rays enter the aperture of a refracting telescope, the biconvex objective lens gathers the rays to a focus at its principal focus and a very small real inverted image of the star is formed there. If the eyepiece lens (another biconvex lens) is arranged so that the small image is at its principal focus, then it will give a very much enlarged distant image at infinity. It

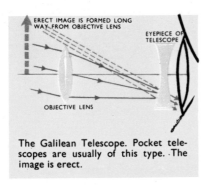

The Galilean Telescope. Pocket telescopes are usually of this type. The image is erect.

may seem strange that the image is no nearer to the observer than the object, but whereas the light rays from the extremities of the object originally arrived at the observer's eye making a small angle with each other, through the telescope the angle they make is much larger and so the image appears to be magnified. The two lenses are placed the sum of their focal lengths apart. The telescope is then said to be in *normal adjustment*. It can also be used with the eyepiece further in so that the small image is inside its focal length. The magnification depends upon the ratio of the focal length of the objective to that of the eyepiece. For a large magnification the objective must have a very long focal length and the eyepiece a very short focal length. There is then a limit to the magnification of portable telescopes because with increased magnification the size of the instrument must increase.

Reflecting Telescopes

Lenses have the disadvantage that they suffer from chromatic and spherical aberration, but these problems are easily eliminated in the reflecting telescopes. Chromatic aberration cannot occur because when light is reflected it is not split up into its component colours as it is on refraction. Spherical aberration can be avoided by making the mirror *parabola* shaped (like the bottom half of an eggshell). This must be accurate to within a millionth of an inch. The largest reflecting telescope in existence – at Mount Palomar, California – has a mirror two hundred inches in diameter. It is made of pyrex glass with a reflecting layer of aluminium deposited on the front surface. This is important because light reflected at the front surface is not absorbed. If the silvering were on the back surface of the mirror, the light would be absorbed by the glass it would have to pass through. The mirror is supported underneath so that it does not sag.

It is usual in modern telescopes to photograph a star under observation instead of looking through the telescope. After several hours sufficient light may come from a star which is invisible to someone looking through the telescope, but which can be seen on a photograph. When this is being done, the telescope uses a clockwork mechanism so that it is continuously trained on the star. This counterbalances the rotation of the Earth which would make the star appear to move.

CHAPTER NINETEEN

The Compound Microscope

THE microscope magnifies objects so that we can see structures that are not normally visible to us. But the purpose of the microscope is not just to produce a magnified image of a small object, it is to distinguish clearly between two particles which are very close together – as two particles, not as one.

When you use a microscope, light must shine through a *partly* transparent object, and its image is then of the observer which is positioned over the eyepiece. Light rays, therefore, pass from the mirror up through the condenser, object, objective lens and eyepiece into the observer's eye.

The power of magnification may vary from about $\times 12$ to $\times 2,000$. The objective contributes most of this. With a $\times 50$ objective and a $\times 4$ eyepiece a magnification of $\times 200$ is obtained. Magnification is the number of times the diameter of the

View under low power

(magnification $\times 15$) Cells scattered in a piece of cartilage.

View under medium power

(magnification $\times 100$) Individual cells can be seen.

View under high power

(magnification $\times 300$) Detail of individual cells can be seen.

enlarged by the lenses (objective and eyepiece) so that it is magnified to your eye.

The mirror reflects light up through the condenser, which is a lens that concentrates light upon the object. The object must be thin and partly transparent to allow light through it and it is normally placed on a glass slide. The objective lens forms a magnified image of the object. This image then becomes the 'object' of the eyepiece lens which magnifies it even more. The newly formed image is then seen by the eye

object is enlarged: $\times 100$ means a hundred times the length and a hundred times the breadth.

Although an ordinary *convex* lens can be used as a microscope, the magnification is limited. However, much larger images can be obtained using a *compound microscope*. In this class of instrument magnification takes place in two stages – the apparatus consists of two lenses or more usually two lens systems.

When a single convex lens is used as a magnifying glass or *simple microscope*, the object has to be situated between the focus of the lens and the lens itself. It is only in this position that a magnified and upright image is formed. Since the light rays only *appear* to come from the image, the image is said to be *virtual*. As will be seen from the diagram, for any one lens, the best magnification is obtained when the distance of the object from the lens is almost equal to the focal length. Greater magnification can be obtained using lenses of shorter focal length, but it is found in practice that objects can be magnified only about a 100 times using a single lens.

The two *convex* lenses (or lens systems) which make up the *compound microscope* are situated at either end of a long tube. The tube serves to exclude all light rays except those reflected by the object. The lens nearest the object is called the *objective*, while the one nearest the eye is the *eyepiece*. Both lenses have short focal lengths. The function of the objective is to form an enlarged and real image which can be further magnified by the eyepiece.

In order that an enlarged and *real* image be formed, the distance of the object from the first lens must be slightly greater than the focal length

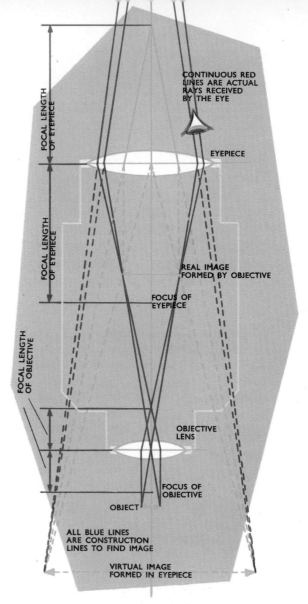

Ray diagram for a compound microscope showing how a real and enlarged image of the object is formed by the objective lens. This image is further magnified by the eyepiece which acts in a similar way to the magnifying glass.

of the lens. If the object is moved further away from the lens, the image is not magnified so much. In fact, if the object distance is more than twice the focal length the image will be smaller than the object. The microscope can, of course, be raised and lowered to bring the image into focus.

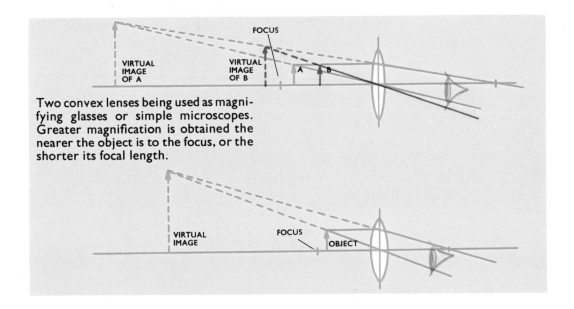

FOCUS

VIRTUAL
IMAGE
OF A

VIRTUAL
IMAGE
OF B

A B

Two convex lenses being used as magnifying glasses or simple microscopes. Greater magnification is obtained the nearer the object is to the focus, or the shorter its focal length.

VIRTUAL
IMAGE

FOCUS

OBJECT

The length of the microscope tube will have been chosen so that the real image formed by the objective is slightly closer to the eyepiece than its principal focus. In this way a *virtual* image larger than its object (the *real* image from the objective lens) is formed by the eyepiece. In fact, the eyepiece is acting like the simple microscope, but in this instance it is magnifying the real image formed by the objective lens.

By using objectives consisting of as many as ten separate lenses and eyepieces with two or more lenses it is possible to magnify over 2,000 times. However, to achieve such high magnification it is essential that the object be very well illuminated, often by a carbon arc lamp.

CHAPTER TWENTY

Diascopes and Epidiascopes

BOTH the slide projector and the epidiascope are designed so that many people are able to see a very much enlarged image projected onto a screen. The slide projector, also called a diascope, gives a stationary picture of a film slide which has been put in it. These projectors form their images from transparent films which resemble in appearance the well-known film negatives. But the ordinary negative cannot be used in a projector, for this will give rise to a peculiar-looking image which is dark where it should be light and light where it should be dark and is in fact a straightforward enlargement of the negative. A *positive* transparency must be used. A source of light is placed behind the film so that the light rays can pass through it and then through a converging lens which forms an image of the film on the screen.

A ray of light falling on a light part of the film slide will pass through it and will later fall on the screen. Another ray of light which is stopped by a dark part of the film will not be able to reach the screen and there will be darkness at that point. The positive film looks very much like an ordinary photograph except that its white areas are transparent.

The theory of how the slide projector works has been given, but in practice certain modifications are needed in its actual construction. Firstly, a very bright and compact

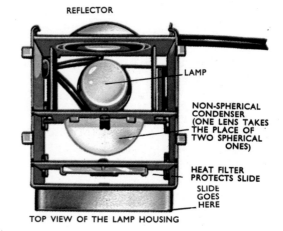

REFLECTOR

LAMP

NON-SPHERICAL CONDENSER (ONE LENS TAKES THE PLACE OF TWO SPHERICAL ONES)

HEAT FILTER PROTECTS SLIDE

SLIDE GOES HERE

TOP VIEW OF THE LAMP HOUSING

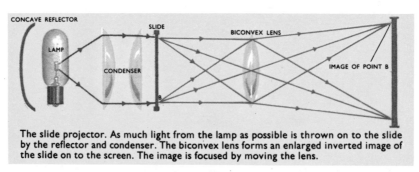

CONCAVE REFLECTOR

LAMP

CONDENSER

SLIDE

BICONVEX LENS

IMAGE OF POINT B

B

The slide projector. As much light from the lamp as possible is thrown on to the slide by the reflector and condenser. The biconvex lens forms an enlarged inverted image of the slide on to the screen. The image is focused by moving the lens.

light source is needed because the screen must be well illuminated. Dark, dim pictures are difficult to see. All the light falling on the screen must have first passed through the transparency. A fairly small screen—say 5 feet by 5 feet (3,600 square inches)—will be about 3,600 times the area of the transparency. So for the required light intensity on the screen the light intensity at the transparency must be 3,600 times as great. Hence the illumination of the transparency must be as efficient as possible. The light source is an incandescent filament lamp whose filament wire is coiled, and then this coil of wire is itself coiled to make a small compact light source. The whole optical system is inside a housing so that light does not escape and a concave mirror is placed behind the lamp to reflect back any light escaping in that direction. The light falls on two plano-convex lenses (known as the condenser). The condenser gathers up light and concentrates it onto the nearby transparency, with the same illumination at the centre as at the edges. A projector without a condenser gives a very dim picture on the screen which is difficult to see and is unevenly illuminated, being much brighter at the middle than at the edges.

Wherever there is light there are also heat rays (infra-red rays). These are very similar to light rays and are only converted into heat whenever they collide with something material. This will happen when these rays come in contact with the film which obviously must not become overheated. Suitably placed air vents and a fan are used to disperse the heat. Nevertheless the instrument will become quite warm because of this effect.

The light rays, having been con-

The Epidiascope

The epidiascope differs in that although it can project images of transparencies (act as a diascope) it also is part episcope. That is, it can use solid objects such as sections of rock and pages of books instead of film to provide the image on the screen. Strong light sources complete with backing mirrors direct light downwards onto the object, from which it is reflected back onto a mirror. The mirror is placed at an angle of 45° to the oncoming light to have the effect of changing its direction by 90° so that it takes a horizontal path. This light passes through a lens system which forms the image on the screen.

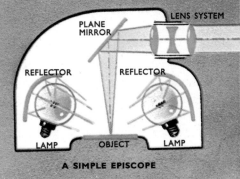

A SIMPLE EPISCOPE

centrated by the condenser, pass through the transparency and fall on the lens of the projector. This lens gathers up the light rays sharply so that those coming from the bottom of the transparency cross over to form an image at the top of the screen and those from the top give an image at the bottom of the screen. So to get an upright image on the screen the transparency must be put in the projector upside-down.

It is usual to screw the lens in or out until the image is properly 'in focus' on the screen.

CHAPTER TWENTY-ONE

Prisms and Periscopes

IT is sometimes necessary to see over or around opaque solid objects which otherwise prevent direct viewing. The commander of a submerged submarine may wish to know if there are any enemy ships within range, people at the back of a crowd want to see what is going on in front of them, while workers in radio-active materials need to observe the apparatus and materials which they are handling by remote control. It is possible to do all this by means of *periscopes*.

The simplest type of periscope consists of a pair of plane mirrors set in the two ends of a tube. The mirrors are arranged so that their surfaces are parallel to one another, and are at a 45° angle to the axis of the tube. This type of periscope is not very satisfactory as there is a tendency for more than one image to form.

A much better instrument is obtained by using a pair of 45° prisms in place of the mirrors. In optics the term prism is usually limited to transparent solids having *triangular* cross-sections. The triangular prisms commonly used in optics are either right-angled (with the other two angles 45° each) or *equilateral* (i.e. have all three sides of equal length and all angles 60°).

In the *submarine periscope* the prisms are arranged as shown in the diagram. Light from the distant object strikes the face of the first prism at right angles (i.e. angle of incidence = 0°). The beam enters the prism without being bent – it has not been *refracted*.

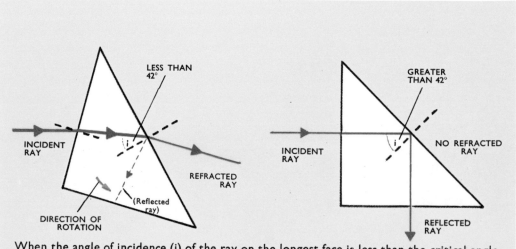

When the angle of incidence (i) of the ray on the longest face is less than the critical angle (42°) most of the light is refracted (left). But if the angle of incidence is greater than the critical angle, all of the light is reflected internally (right). Total internal reflection can only occur if the ray is in the denser medium.

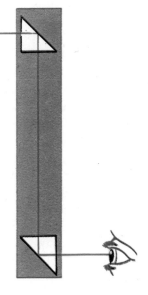

The long side of the triangle then acts as a plane mirror for rays already within the prism, provided that the angle at which the rays strike the mirror surface is greater than the *critical angle.*

The angle of incidence of the beam on the reflecting surface is 45°, and as the angle of incidence is equal to the angle of reflection, the beam is reflected at 45° to the normal. This ray has, therefore, been turned through a right angle and will strike the third side of the triangle at right angles. The beam passes straight out of the prism without being refracted. The beam undergoes similar reflection at the second 45° prism, and emerges from the periscope parallel with the original incident beam.

The importance of the beam of light striking the first face of the prism at right angles can be shown by a simple experiment. A narrow parallel beam of light is directed at a 45° prism so that it is as nearly as possible at right angles to a short face. At first the beam is reflected in the same way as in the periscope, and emerges from the other short face at right angles to its original path. But if the prism is very slowly rotated a position is suddenly reached when the beam is no longer *totally* reflected by the longer face. Instead most of the light is *refracted* at the latter face and light emerges from that face. The angle of incidence at which this change occurs is known as the *critical angle.* For

The Submarine Periscope incorporates two 45° prisms. These are better than mirrors because the formation of multiple images is avoided.

ordinary (Crown) glass the critical angle for light travelling from glass to air is 42°

In passing from a more dense to a less dense medium (*e.g.,* from glass to air), a beam of light is bent (*refracted*) away from the normal. If the angle of incidence (in the denser medium) is greater than the critical angle, *all* the light is *reflected internally* instead of being refracted. If the angle of incidence is being increased, just before the critical angle is reached, the angle of refraction (in the less dense medium) is almost a right angle. Total internal reflection only occurs when light travelling in a more dense medium strikes the boundary of a less dense medium. It cannot occur for light going from a less dense medium into a more dense medium.

CHAPTER TWENTY-TWO

The Camera

A CAMERA is little more than a light-tight box with a hole in the front and a roll of light-sensitive paper at the back on which the picture of objects in front of the camera can fall. Afterwards, the film can be developed and prints can be made from the negative (the developed film).

This is the basic camera, but cameras are, of course, more complicated than this. Additional modifications are added to improve the quality of the picture. Nevertheless, it is possible to take a quite reasonable photograph using this very simple type of *pinhole* camera. When the photograph is

being taken, light can enter the camera through the small hole in the front of the box. When not in use, this hole can be sealed off with a piece of black sticky tape. Rays of light either from the sun or from an artificial source strike the object being photographed and are then reflected away from it. Light cannot turn corners. The rays travel on in the direction in which they have been reflected. Some of these rays enter through the pinhole in the camera. Rays from the top of the object will hit the bottom of the film and those from the bottom of the object will

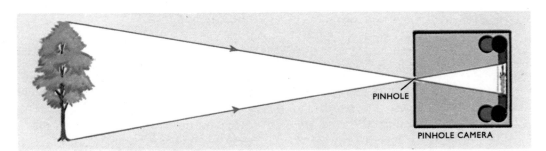

To take a photograph of a tree thirty feet high using a pinhole camera and obtain an image on the film about two inches high the photograph must be taken about ninety feet away from the tree. Close-up pictures of large objects are impossible.

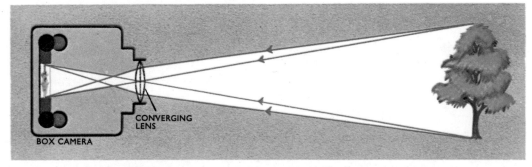

The lens of this box camera gathers up the light rays leaving the distant tree to form a sharp image on the film at the back of the camera.

hit the top of the film. In this fashion an inverted image is formed on the film. To get a clear image the pinhole must be small, and as it is so small very little light can enter to affect the film. The pinhole must then be left open for several minutes (long exposure) for sufficient light to enter the camera. Distant, immovable objects are the best subjects for this type of photography. Sharp pictures can only be obtained for stationary distant objects under fairly bright conditions.

It is not always convenient to have the film exposed for such a long time. When people are being photographed they find it difficult to stand still for long and the slightest movement will show as a blur on the picture. In the *box camera* a converging lens which is about one third of an inch in dia-

meter is mounted inside the aperture (opening) to gather the light rays coming from the object and focus them on the film at the back of the camera. The distance between the lens and the film is fixed and is equal to the focal length of the lens (i.e. the distance from its lens to its principal focus). This means that rays from very distant objects will converge on the film, but rays from near objects will tend to converge behind the film. As a rule it will give a good image only of objects more than about six feet away.

Advances on the Simple Box Camera

The extra cost of the more expensive cameras is taken up to some extent by better quality lenses, but also by the various adjusting mechanisms

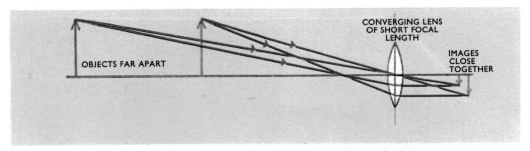

Box camera with lens of short focal length. Although the two objects are some distance apart, the two images are very close together. This trick is used in the box camera so that it will focus clearly over a large range without moving the lens.

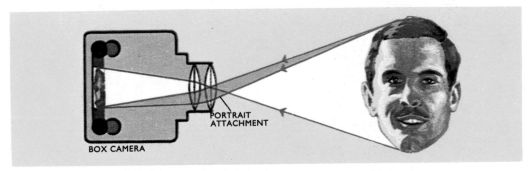

The portrait attachment for a box camera is an additional converging lens. The combination of two lenses bends the light more sharply so that a near object can be photographed.

which allow the cameras to be used under more varied conditions. The simplest adjustment is one of focusing. On a folding camera this may be done by sliding the bellows in and out and altering the distance between lens and film. This method is now uncommon and a more usual method is to mount the lens in a screw thread. By screwing the lens in and out, it is possible to bring objects at various distances into sharp focus on the film.

A film will give a good picture only if it is correctly exposed – i.e. if the correct amount of light falls on it. This is why a simple box camera with an ordinary medium speed film can be used only in bright light. A camera with an adjustable aperture and/or shutter can be used in poorer light conditions, however, with the same film. By increasing the size of the

aperture or the time for which the shutter stays open, more light can be made to fall on the film. The amount of light falling on the film depends upon the size of the aperture and the time for which the shutter opens.

An adjustable aperture or iris diaphragm consists of a set of metal 'leaves' set in a circle. They can be adjusted to give any required aperture. The aperture and the shutter are complementary features. Under given conditions, a smaller aperture needs a longer shutter exposure and vice-versa. The adjustable aperture allows sufficient light in, even when the shutter is open for only a very short period of time – such as is necessary to take pictures of fast-moving objects.

The size of the aperture can be set at any value but there are a

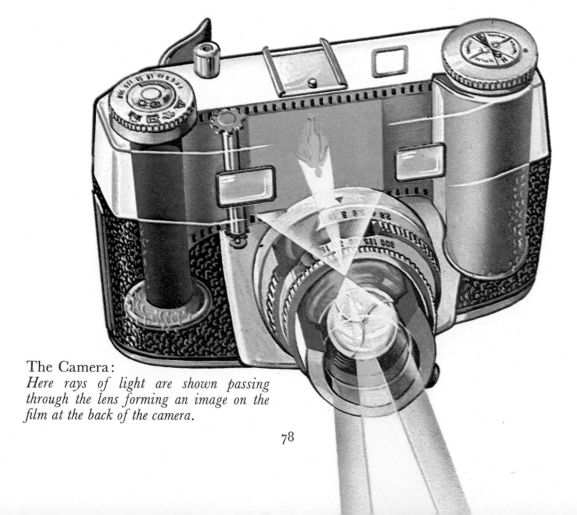

The Camera:
Here rays of light are shown passing through the lens forming an image on the film at the back of the camera.

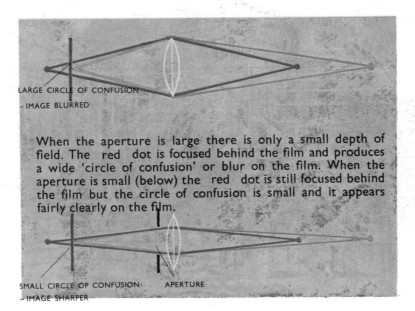

LARGE CIRCLE OF CONFUSION
– IMAGE BLURRED

When the aperture is large there is only a small depth of field. The red dot is focused behind the film and produces a wide 'circle of confusion' or blur on the film. When the aperture is small (below) the red dot is still focused behind the film but the circle of confusion is small and it appears fairly clearly on the film.

SMALL CIRCLE OF CONFUSION   APERTURE
– IMAGE SHARPER

IMAGE IN FOCUS

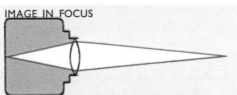

With the lens in the correct position the image is in focus on the film.

IMAGE OUT OF FOCUS

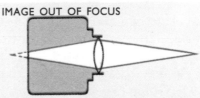

For this object, which is nearer the lens, the image is blurred. To make the image appear in focus the lens must be screwed outwards.

The diaphragm which is made of over-lapping leaves controls the amount of light entering the camera and stops the outer rays from passing through the lens. This also cuts down distortion of the image due to spherical aberration.

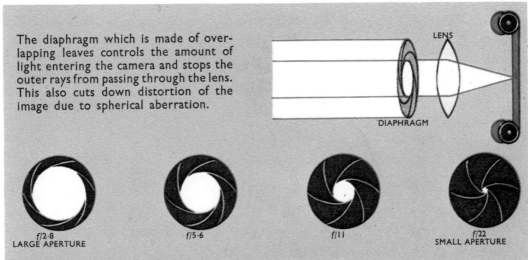

LENS

DIAPHRAGM

f/2·8
LARGE APERTURE

f/5·6

f/11

f/22
SMALL APERTURE

The diaphragm can be adjusted to alter the size of the aperture. A large aperture is used on a dull day and a small one on a bright day.

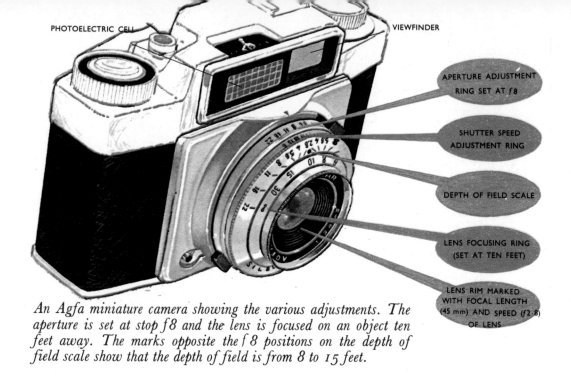

APERTURE ADJUSTMENT
RING SET AT *f* 8

SHUTTER SPEED
ADJUSTMENT RING

DEPTH OF FIELD SCALE

LENS FOCUSING RING
(SET AT TEN FEET)

LENS RIM MARKED
WITH FOCAL LENGTH
(45 mm) AND SPEED (*f* 2·8)
OF LENS

An Agfa miniature camera showing the various adjustments. The aperture is set at stop f8 and the lens is focused on an object ten feet away. The marks opposite the f 8 positions on the depth of field scale show that the depth of field is from 8 to 15 feet.

number of recognized settings (*stops or f-numbers*) that are marked on the aperture adjustment ring. On a typical camera these may run from 2·8 to 22. Going up the scale from one number to the next halves the amount of light going through. In other words, it halves the effective speed of the lens. The exposure time must be doubled therefore for a correct exposure.

There is, however, another very important point to remember about apertures. The aperture controls the *depth of field.* If the camera is focused on an object fifteen feet away, some objects nearer and farther away will also be in focus. If the aperture is wide open there will only be a small depth of field – say between fourteen and sixteen feet. But if the photographer *stops down* (i.e., closes the aperture) to say *f*8 then the depth of focus may be from eight feet to thirty feet. The depth depends also on the focal length of the lens and the distance of the object being photographed. When · the aperture is reduced, the cone of light reaching

the film is narrow and blurring is less apparent. More objects then appear to be in focus.

The lens of a simple camera consists of a single convex piece of glass (or even plastic) which focuses light from the object onto the film. All simple lenses suffer from defects, however, which tend to distort the image. All but the cheapest cameras have *compound* lenses made up of two or more elements. These are chosen so that most of their individual defects are corrected by another element. A really good camera lens may have six or more elements.

Other refinements on the more expensive cameras include coupled exposure-meters, rangefinders, flash equipment, counters to indicate the number of exposures used or remaining, and delayed action mechanisms which enable the photographer to press the button and get into the group before the shutter opens. All of these refinements help to avoid failures or to take special pictures but none is essential.

The Colours of Light

CHAPTER TWENTY-THREE

Spectra and Spectroscopes

SPECTRA

THE light from the Sun, or the light given out by a carbon arc lamp, appears to be white, but a closer examination of this white light will reveal that it does, in fact, consist of a mixture of rays of several different colours. Sometimes, on a bright sunny day, a *spectrum* of lights of different colours may be noticed on the wall of a room away from the window. With care, the path of this light can be traced back to its source, and it will, in all probability, be found that white light has been broken up into its constituent parts as a result of refraction at a glass edge—the corner of a mirror, or perhaps an ornament or a cut-glass

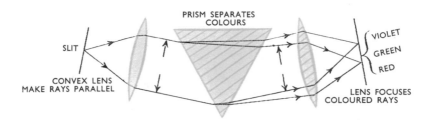

Ray diagram showing how the spectrum (below) is produced. The light rays are made parallel by the first lens, split into colours by the prism and focused by the second lens.

82

vase.

A similar effect may be observed in a darkened room if a narrow beam of white light is directed on to a triangular glass prism. If a white screen is held in the path of the light emerging from the prism a number of coloured bands of light are noticed. It is found that white light is made up from light of the following colours – violet, indigo, blue, green, yellow, orange, and red.

A prism is able to separate white light into its colours because the various coloured rays have different wavelengths. Of the visible forms violet light has the shortest wavelength and is refracted by the greatest

Some emission spectra. (Top) *Spectrum of hydrogen.* (Middle) *Spectrum of mercury.* (Bottom) *Spectrum of white light from a carbon arc lamp.*

amount on passing through the prism (i.e. the violet is deviated most violently). Red light has the greatest wavelength of all colours in the visible spectrum and is refracted by the least amount.

SPECTROSCOPES

A triangular glass prism is, in fact, the simplest type of *spectroscope* for splitting light into its component colours. But it is of little practical value because the coloured images of the light source merge with one another. Modern spectroscopes, although they still use the

prism to split the light, have certain modifications to make the splitting more complete. A special screen is put in front of the light source to control the light falling on the prism. In the screen is a very thin parallel-sided slit which allows only a thin sliver of light to pass through. The slit width is adjustable.

The illuminated slip is the object under observation in the spectroscope and the light shining on it is the light being examined by the spectroscope. A system of lenses (corrected for chromatic aberration and other defects), called a *collimator*, is placed so that the slit is at its focus. This makes all the individual beams in the slit of light parallel to each other on leaving the collimator. The beam of parallel light rays falls on the prism. The light is bent or refracted on entering the prism and again on leaving it. Light of long wavelength (e.g. red light) is bent least; light of smaller wavelength (e.g. violet light) is bent more sharply. Bands of coloured light fan out from the prism and each type of light is brought into focus by a converging lens similar to a camera lens. Each type of light present is made to form a real image of the slit in its own colour. As the original object slit is so thin its image for, say, blue light is a thin blue line. If the object slit had been curved, then the image would also be curved, but in practice this is never done and the line-shaped images are often spoken of as spectral lines. A telescope eyepiece can be used to view the images or a photographic plate used instead. When a photographic plate is used the instrument is a *spectrograph*.

In practice the collimator is housed in a tube with the object slit at one end and the other end directed towards the prism. This is called the collimator arm of the apparatus. The prism is placed on a turntable and the image is viewed through the movable telescope arm of the apparatus, a tube housing the focusing lens and the eyepiece. The light source is placed in front of the slit.

If any element is made hot enough to be incandescent and is then used as a light source to be analysed by a spectroscope, several lines corresponding to light of particular wavelengths will be seen through the telescope. For a particular chemical element the picture will always be the same. Each

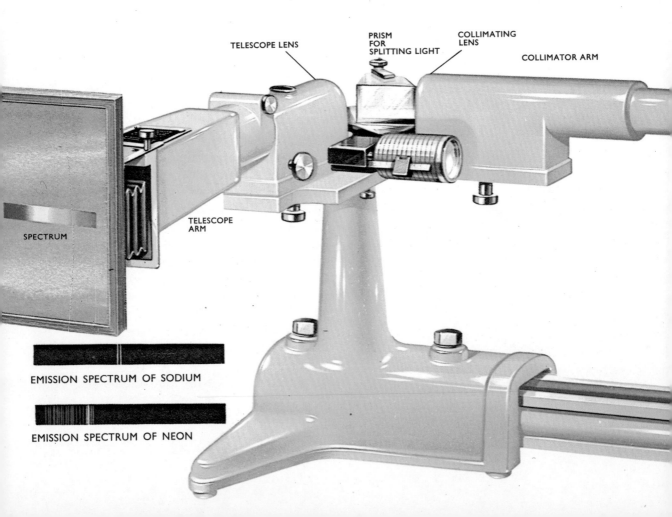

SPECTRUM

TELESCOPE LENS

PRISM FOR SPLITTING LIGHT

COLLIMATING LENS

COLLIMATOR ARM

TELESCOPE ARM

EMISSION SPECTRUM OF SODIUM

EMISSION SPECTRUM OF NEON

element has its own characteristic spectrum. A man can be identified by his fingerprints; an element can be identified by its spectrum.

Absorption and Emission Spectra

Hydrogen, the atom with the least electrons, has the simplest spectrum. An atom with more electrons will have a more complicated spectrum. When an atom is heated, its electrons can absorb 'packets' of energy which allows them to jump out to another shell where the electrons are more 'energetic'. The atom is said to be in an excited state. On cooling, the electrons can jump back into their original positions, and in doing so each electron emits light of a particular wavelength. This light can be analysed to find the *emission spectrum* of the element.

Certain elements give out certain wavelengths of light during emission. When light falls on an element it can absorb light of the *same* wavelengths as it emits when it is excited. This is called absorption. It is possible to obtain both the emission spectrum and the absorption spectrum of an element. The absorption spectrum will be a range of colour with black lines indicating the wavelengths of light which have been absorbed by the element and which therefore show as 'gaps' in the complete spectrum – black being the absence of light. These black lines correspond exactly to the coloured lines in the emission

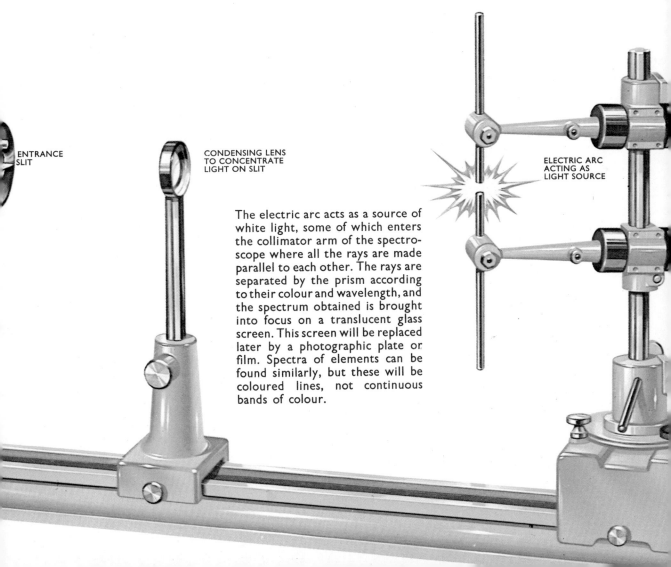

ENTRANCE
SLIT

CONDENSING LENS
TO CONCENTRATE
LIGHT ON SLIT

ELECTRIC ARC
ACTING AS
LIGHT SOURCE

The electric arc acts as a source of white light, some of which enters the collimator arm of the spectroscope where all the rays are made parallel to each other. The rays are separated by the prism according to their colour and wavelength, and the spectrum obtained is brought into focus on a translucent glass screen. This screen will be replaced later by a photographic plate or film. Spectra of elements can be found similarly, but these will be coloured lines, not continuous bands of colour.

spectrum. The emission spectrum will be black (i.e., an absence of light of wavelengths not emitted by the particular element), with coloured lines indicating particular wavelengths of light. There are certain dark lines or missing wavelengths in the spectrum of the Sun. These dark lines are called *Fraunhofer lines* and are named after Joseph von Fraunhofer, the German scientist who discovered them. They are caused by the presence of certain elements in the gases surrounding the Sun which are cooler than the Sun. They absorb the energy they need to make them excited from the Sun's rays and in doing so make gaps in the spectrum. By examining the spectra of individual elements it was possible to discover the elements responsible for these gaps.

The Use of the Spectroscope

The spectroscope has great uses in astronomy. The spectra of stars give considerable information about the gases surrounding them. In some cases where there should be only one line missing, there are in fact two very close together. This splitting is due to the magnetic effect of the star and so the spectrum can be used to discover information about the magnetic fields of stars. Sometimes the spectrum lines have been moved up a little, either towards the red or towards the violet end of the spectrum. From this shift the speed and direction of travel of the star can be calculated. Spectroscopes are also used in chemical analysis, where spectrum lines can reveal the presence of certain elements and of certain groups of elements in molecules.

A good spectroscope should be capable of producing two separate spectrum lines for two wavelengths which differ only slightly. It should space these two lines as far apart as possible instead of blurring and overlapping them. If an extremely fine mesh or grating is used in place of the prism then better separation of lines is obtained. The lines produced by a grating, however, are not usually as bright as those produced by a prism.

CHAPTER TWENTY-FOUR

The Rainbow

THE soft bands of colour spanning the sky were once veiled in mystery but now there is a simple scientific explanation for rainbows.

For a rainbow to be formed, certain weather conditions are necessary. The day must be sunny and the sun quite low in the sky. There are no noon-day rainbows where the sun is directly overhead. The best times are in the morning or evening. Nor is it possible to see a rainbow while facing the sun. The person seeing the rainbow always has his back towards it. Some distance in front of him it is raining. It is obvious that the raindrops are responsible for this coloured effect because it is equally possible for rainbows to be formed under suitable conditions by waterfalls, fountains or the spray from a garden hose.

The sunlight falling on the rain consists of a colourless (white) mixture of radiation of various wavelengths. Red light has the longest wavelength and violet light the shortest. Raindrops are almost spherical, held in shape by forces acting on their surfaces (*surface tension forces*) and behave like lenses. As a ray of light enters a water droplet, it is bent (*refracted*). The violet light is bent the most and the red light not as much. The effect of this is to split the white light into its component colours. When the radiation reaches the far side of the droplet some leaves the droplet but the surface reflects part back into the droplet. Again when the reflected light encounters the surface, some radiation is refracted as it leaves and the rest is reflected. With this refraction, as light is passing from water to air, the red light is bent more than the violet. As can be seen from the diagram, the red light comes into the observer's eye at a larger angle to the horizontal than the violet light, *i.e.* the red seems to come from higher up than the violet.

Because of this, the top of the rainbow appears red and the bottom

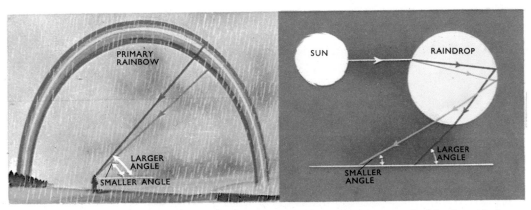

Primary rainbows are formed by light which has been reflected once inside the raindrops.

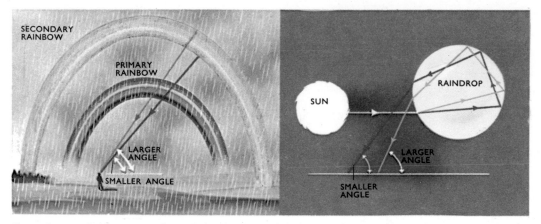

Secondary rainbows are formed by light which has undergone two reflections inside the raindrops.

violet. Such a rainbow is known as a *primary rainbow*. It is formed by light which has only been reflected once inside the water droplets. Individual colours of the spectrum reaching one observer come from different raindrops.

Double rainbows are sometimes seen. There is a bright primary rainbow (red at the top, purple underneath) and some distance above it another much fainter *secondary rainbow*. This time the colours are reversed. The purple is at the top and the red at the bottom. Secondary rainbows are formed by light which has been reflected twice inside the raindrops. After two reflections, the violet light makes a larger angle with the horizontal at the observer's eye than does the red light. Therefore this time the purple seems higher up than the red. When the primary rainbow is very faint it is often impossible to see the secondary rainbow.

When the sun is low in the sky, the light leaving the droplets comes back to Earth where it can be picked up by the observer. But if the sun is high in the sky, the emerging light does not come back to Earth and consequently no rainbow is seen.

When the sun is high in the sky it is impossible to see a rainbow. Light emerging from the water droplets does not reach the observer.

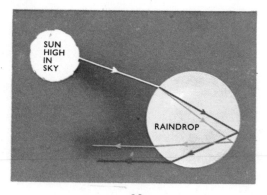

CHAPTER TWENTY-FIVE

The Colour of the Sky

IF the Earth had no atmosphere, the sky would appear completely black except in the direction of the Sun. But the Earth has an atmosphere, which redirects or *scatters* sunlight so that light appears to come, not just from the Sun's bright disc, but from all parts of the sky. On a cloudless day, the sky is blue.

Most of the atmosphere is fairly transparent to visible light, and lets sunlight carry on to strike the Earth. If the atmosphere were completely transparent, we should not see it at all (i.e. the sky would appear black). Only when light is scattered can it be seen.

In the same way, a shaft of sunlight passing into a darkened room is made visible by dust particles in the air. A small proportion of the sunlight hits the dust particles, and 'bounces' off them in all directions. The tiny particles reflect some of the light directly into the eyes of the observer, and light scattered like this from all parts of the light beam defines its shape. If the room were dust-free, the observer would be unable to detect the beam.

Molecules of air can also scatter light, but, since they are very much smaller than dust particles, and less likely to affect a beam of light, the scattering must take place on a very large scale to be visible at all.

This happens in the atmosphere. A small amount of sunlight is scattered by gas molecules and there are such an enormous number of them in the atmosphere that the scattered light is easily observable.

The sky is blue because light at the blue end of the spectrum is scattered more easily than light at the red end. Molecules are more selective than dust particles in the way they scatter light. Dust particles tend to scatter all colours indiscriminately so that the scattered light is white. Scattering by molecules is dependent on the colour of the light. Lord Rayleigh (1842–1919) developed a theory of scattering, and worked out that blue light should be scattered about ten times more readily than red light.

The scattering by the atmosphere also explains why the Sun's disc becomes red at sunset. Sunlight is striking the Earth at an angle, and it

This is how the Sun would appear if the Earth had no light-scattering atmosphere. All the light rays come direct from the Sun.

Some of the Sun's blue light is scattered by the atmosphere. Blue light comes from the atmosphere, and gives its blue colour.

has to travel through an extra long distance through the denser parts of the atmosphere. More blue light than red light is scattered out of the direct sunlight by the atmosphere. The white light loses some of its blue light, so it appears, on balance, red.

After sunset, light cannot come directly from the sun. Twilight is light scattered by the atmosphere on to the **dark side of the Earth. Astronauts orbiting the Earth have measured** the extent of the twilight zone, and it is possible to deduce from their observations that the layer of the Earth's atmosphere mainly responsible for the scattering is about 16 miles above its surface.

The upper observer sees the mid-day sky. His eyes receive both direct, white light from the Sun and blue light scattered by the atmosphere. At the same time the lower observer sees the sunrise. Sunlight reaching his eyes has had to travel a much longer distance through the light-scattering layers. Both blue and green light are scattered, so the direct sunlight appears reddish.

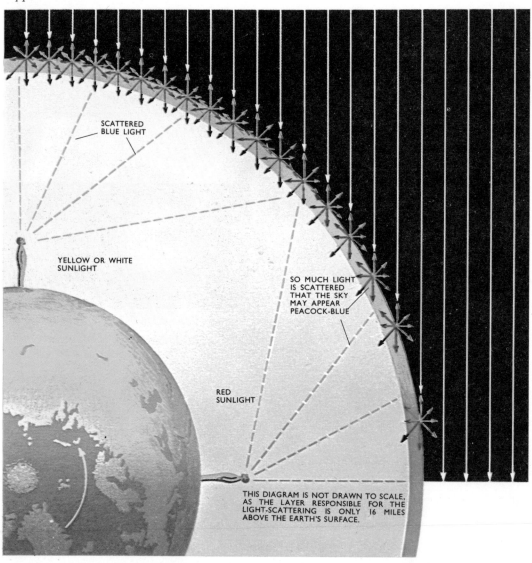

SCATTERED BLUE LIGHT

YELLOW OR WHITE SUNLIGHT

SO MUCH LIGHT IS SCATTERED THAT THE SKY MAY APPEAR PEACOCK-BLUE

RED SUNLIGHT

THIS DIAGRAM IS NOT DRAWN TO SCALE, AS THE LAYER RESPONSIBLE FOR THE LIGHT-SCATTERING IS ONLY 16 MILES ABOVE THE EARTH'S SURFACE.

CHAPTER TWENTY-SIX

Colour Filters

AN ordinary transparent glass windowpane lets practically all the light striking it pass through. But coloured glass transmits only a portion. Red glass lets through mainly red light, blue glass mainly blue, and so on. Light rays entering the coloured glass are *filtered*, some of them being absorbed and a certain number being allowed to filter through. A yellow glass filter, for instance, may let through some green, orange and red light as well as yellow, but it absorbs these other colours more than it absorbs yellow. So the overall appearance of light transmitted through a yellow filter is yellow.

Combinations of colour filters can change the appearance of a beam of light. Take, for example, the combination of red and green filters. One transmits mainly red and the other mainly green. So a combination of the two will transmit hardly any light at all.

Colour filters are often used in black-and-white photography. The filter, a disc of stained glass with polished parallel sides, is attached in front of the lens of the camera to stop part of the light from reaching the light-sensitive paper inside. A pale yellow filter makes daylight scenes appear, in black-and-white, more realistic. This filter transmits all the colours of the spectrum from the red to the green, absorbing a little of the blue and violet, and absorbing all the invisible rays beyond the violet—the ultra-violet rays. Al-

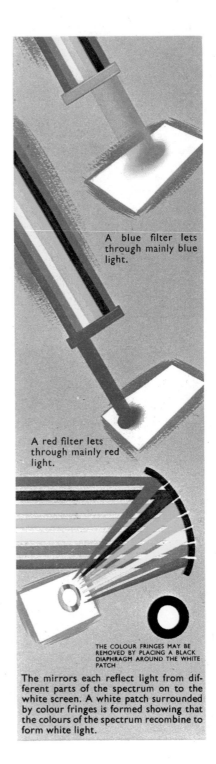

A blue filter lets through mainly blue light.

A red filter lets through mainly red light.

THE COLOUR FRINGES MAY BE REMOVED BY PLACING A BLACK DIAPHRAGM AROUND THE WHITE PATCH

The mirrors each reflect light from different parts of the spectrum on to the white screen. A white patch surrounded by colour fringes is formed showing that the colours of the spectrum recombine to form white light.

The scene on the left photographed without (centre) and with (right) a pale yellow colour filter.

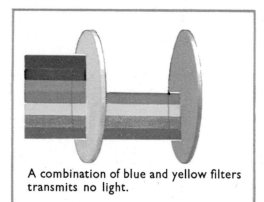

A combination of blue and yellow filters transmits no light.

snow—will contain ultra-violet rays. Without the filter these rays would blacken the photographic negative, so that the black-and-white *positive* print shows the sky or snow to be *lighter* than they appeared to the eye. The pale yellow filter corrects the balance of light and shade in the photograph by supplying the camera with only the visible colours.

A darker yellow filter cuts out more of the blue and violet end of the spectrum. Since less blue light now reaches the camera, blue objects appear darker on the final print, or positive. White cloud formations will stand out more starkly against the darker background.

though these rays cannot be seen by the eye, they may be detected by the photographic paper. Light reaching the camera from bright blue or white objects—a blue sky or white

CHAPTER TWENTY-SEVEN

Colour Mixing

THE white spotlight picks out the white dress of the dancer on the stage. To the audience the dress appears white. But if the spotlights are changed to blue, red, green, or any other colour, the dress will apparently change its colour and take the colour of the spotlight illuminating it.

The dancer's white dress appears as white because it reflects to the eyes of the audience the white of the spotlight. But a white object appears white only because it reflects *all* the light falling on it. When the spotlight is changed to red only red light falls on the dress and so only red light can be reflected. The dress will reflect blue light and appear blue, green light and appear green. To make the dress appear any colour of the spectrum however, need not necessarily mean a large number of different spotlights, each giving a beam of a different colour. In fact any colour effect can be produced by mixing the beams from three spotlights – red, blue and green. These are the three *primary* colours of light. By mixing the beams in the right proportion, any visible colour can be made. A red spotlight and a green spotlight of equal intensity on the white dress, surprisingly enough, make it appear yellow. Add a blue spotlight and the dress becomes white again.

White light from the Sun or from the spotlight is itself a mixture of light of different colours. This can be seen by passing the light through a prism where the light is split up into its constituent colours. But as the different colours of white light can be separated, so they can be added together again. The mixing of all the colours of the spectrum will naturally give white light again. The mixing of any two colours will give a third colour, and the mixing of the three special, or primary, colours will give the appearance of white light. Thus white light, which can be seen by the prism-splitting to be a mixture of a great many different colours can be effectively reduced to a mixture of the three primaries, red, blue and green. The colour 'triangle' (see next page) is a convenient method for remembering the results of mixing lights of particular colours. The combination of two colours at the corners of the triangle gives the colour in between. Colours opposite each other in the triangle are called *complementary* colours. Their special property is that they will combine together to give white light again.

These are the colour effects produced by mixing different beams of light of different colours, and watching their effect on a white object, which reflects light of all colours equally. A different effect accounts for the fact that a red object is red. The red object does not appear red because it produces light on its own, as the red spotlight did. It appears to have a particular colour because it *reflects* this colour to the audience. When the dancer wore a white dress it reflected all the white light from the white spotlight and so appeared white. If she changed into a red dress she would appear red under the same white spotlight. This is because red substances sort out the red part in the white light and reflect it back. They absorb all the rest, *i.e.* the blue and the green. Red light falling on a red dress is completely reflected – none is absorbed. But if the red dress is illuminated by light of either of the other two primary colours, it will appear black, or merge into the dark surroundings. The red colouring

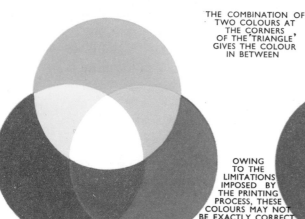

THE COMBINATION OF TWO COLOURS AT THE CORNERS OF THE 'TRIANGLE' GIVES THE COLOUR IN BETWEEN

OWING TO THE LIMITATIONS IMPOSED BY THE PRINTING PROCESS, THESE COLOURS MAY NOT BE EXACTLY CORRECT.

The additive colour 'triangle' of light.   *The subtractive 'triangle' of pigments.*

matter will absorb all the blue or all the green light, leaving none to reflect back to the watching audience. Any object from which no light is reflected appears, of course, black.

As the three primary colours of light could be mixed together to produce a beam of light of any colour, so there are three pigments (colouring matters, *e.g.* paints) which when mixed together produce a pigment capable of absorbing light of any colour. The three 'primary' pigments are not the same as the

The dancer's white dress on the left changes colour as the spotlights are changed. When lit by red, green and blue lights together, the dress appears white again. A red dress (on the right) turns black under blue or green light.

three primary colours of light. They are in fact yellow, magenta and blue-green – the secondary colours of light. Each pigment 'primary' *absorbs* one of the primary colours of light and reflects the other two.

Yellow is one of the pigment 'primaries'. A yellow dress in a white spotlight (which is equivalent to a mixture of red, green and blue spotlights) reflects the two colours of light which make up yellow – red and green. It absorbs all the blue, the complementary colour of yellow.

A blue-green dress reflects blue and green and absorbs all the red. So if yellow and blue-green pigments are mixed in equal proportions, the resultant pigment absorbs all light but green, which is reflected. Thus yellow paint mixed with blue-green paint gives green paint.

The colour of any pigment is the result of *subtracting* from the white light all the colours the constituent pigments absorb, and reflecting only the colours common to all the constituents. All reflected light can be

95

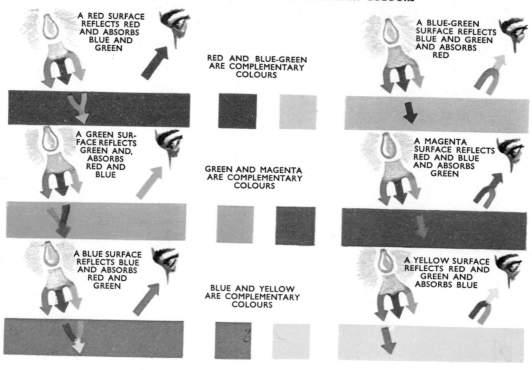

eliminated by mixing green and magenta pigments. The magenta will reflect only red and blue and the green will reflect only green. There are no colours common to both pigments which can possibly be reflected, and the object appears black. The colours must, however, be mixed in the right proportions. If there is more green than magenta, some green light will not be absorbed by the magenta, so the mixed pigment appears dark green. The complementary pigments are red and blue-green, green and magenta, blue and yellow. But unlike the mixing of coloured lights, the sum of two complementary pigments is black. Complementary colours of light appear white when mixed in the correct proportions because the beam of light contains *all* the constituents of white light. Complementary *pigments* appear black when mixed because a substance has thus been produced which will *absorb all* the constituent parts of white light. The pigment has subtracted from white light all the colours which can be absorbed, and has left none to reflect.

Light Waves in Action

CHAPTER TWENTY-EIGHT
Interference

SIR ISAAC NEWTON showed that 'white light', daylight, or the light from a lamp is really composed of light of a number of different colours. White light can be split up by a prism into these colours, because the light of each different colour travels at a slightly different speed through the prism. They are bent or refracted by differing amounts, so, when the beam of light is focused on to a screen, each of the different colours arrives at a different place. The band of colours is called the *spectrum*.

In later experiments, Newton found different ways of producing the spectrum. He put a lens from a large telescope on top of a flat sheet of glass. The lens was illuminated by light from the Sun and Newton was investigating the sunlight reflected by the lens and glass. Looking down at the lens, Newton saw all the colours of the spectrum, arranged in concentric rings around

Some of the light is reflected by the lens and some by the mirror. Waves of light travel slightly different distances, so become 'out of step'. Each colour of light has its own wavelength, so becomes out of step at a different place.

the centre of the lens. The colours were sharp near the centre, but they became fuzzier nearer the edges. The circular spectra had been produced by separating white light from the lamp into its different colours, but this had been done in an entirely different way from the splitting of light in a prism.

The process by which the colours had been apparently separated is called *interference*. Between the lens and the flat glass, the beam of light had been divided into two definite parts. One part was reflected at the lower surface of the lens (this was a gently curved surface). The other had not been reflected at this surface, but had passed through the tiny bit of air space between lens and flat glass, and had been reflected by the flat glass. Both beams were reflected back towards the eye. Where they met in the lens, they had *interfered* with one

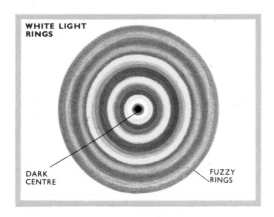

Newton's Rings appear as circles if the observer is directly above the lens. With white light, they are coloured.

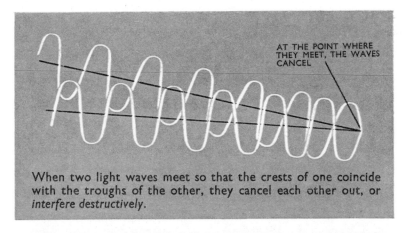

When two light waves meet so that the crests of one coincide with the troughs of the other, they cancel each other out, or *interfere destructively*.

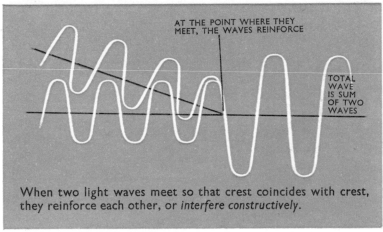

When two light waves meet so that crest coincides with crest, they reinforce each other, or *interfere constructively*.

another.

Interference can cause patterns of light and darkness because of the peculiar nature of light. Light, like sound or radio signals, is a form of energy carried by *waves*. As light travels in straight lines at the phenomenal speed of 186,000 miles a second, its waves vibrate up and down about 500,000,000,000,000 times a second. This vibration stimulates the retinas of our eyes.

If the waves in two beams of light go up and come down together, they reinforce each other, and the intensity of a combined light beam is increased. The two beams are said to be *in phase*. But if two light beams are mixed so that the 'ups' of one coincide with the 'downs' of the other (i.e. they are *out of phase*), the ups and downs will cancel out, and the beam of light will disappear. When waves reinforce, it is called *constructive interference*, and when they cancel out, *destructive interference*.

Interference of light is difficult to detect since its waves are so very small and vibrate so rapidly. However, interference takes place with any kind of wave motion, and the effects of interference can be more easily seen by examining the behaviour of water waves, which are in many ways similar to light waves, but travel more slowly and are more easily noticeable.

Water waves spread out from a dis-

DOUBLE CRESTS—
A CREST COINCIDES
WITH A CREST
FLATTENED REGION—
A CREST COINCIDES
WITH A TROUGH

Wherever a crest coincides with a trough, the water surface is flattened.

turbance in the centre of a pond as light waves spread out from a light bulb. If there are two disturbances in the same pond, waves from one interfere with waves from another. Where the crests of one meet the troughs of another, the waves disappear.

An essential feature of the Newton's

Rings experiment is that both the beams of light come from the same source. Then, when the light leaves the source all the crests occur at the same time and all the troughs occur at the same time. But the beam which goes on straight through the lens and is reflected by the flat glass travels an extra distance. When it rejoins the

A beam of light of one colour (one wavelength) hits the lens, and passes through the first surface of the lens, and strikes the curved surface.

Part of it is reflected to hit the eye from the curved surface. But some goes on to hit the flat mirror surface.

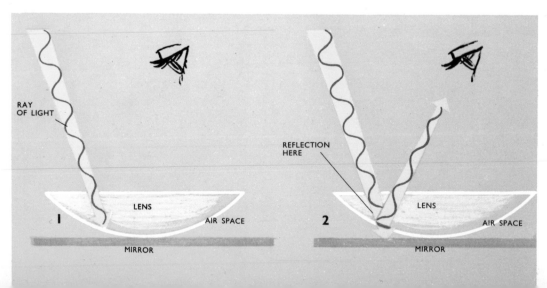

RAY
OF LIGHT

REFLECTION
HERE

LENS

LENS

AIR SPACE

AIR SPACE

1

2

MIRROR

MIRROR

other light beam it is out of step with it. The amount it is out of step depends on the extra distance it has travelled, so that all the beams arriving at points the same distance from the central axis of the lens will arrive in the same state. If they are half a wave out of step, crest cancels trough, so all points where the extra distance travelled has made them half a wavelength out of step are dark. The points all lie on a circle.

Newton's experiment was complicated because he used white light, a mixture of light of different wavelengths. Even if the extra distance travelled means that light of one colour (one wavelength) is exactly half a wave out of step, the other colours are not exactly half a wave out of step. Only one colour is half a wave out of step at a time. If, for example, this colour is red, the light appears blue (i.e. the appearance of a beam of white light with the red part removed).

The rings can be seen much better when, instead of white light, *monochromatic*, or *one-colour* light is used. A convenient source is a Bunsen burner

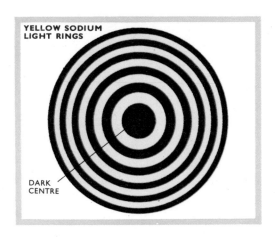

If the light of one colour is used, the dark rings become more distinct. The distance between then depends on the wavelength.

flame with a piece of paper soaked in brine wrapped round it. The brine contains sodium (common salt is sodium chloride) and the flame is a bright sodium yellow.

In this light, the rings are bright yellow, separated by sharp dark rings. Waves of yellow light, when exactly in step, produce bright rings. When they are exactly out of step, they produce

Where the two parts of the wave combine, they interfere with each other. These two waves are in step, so interfere constructively.

At a different part of the lens, the two parts interfere destructively. They are a complete wavelength out of step.

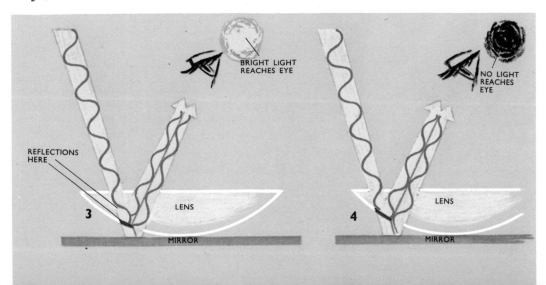

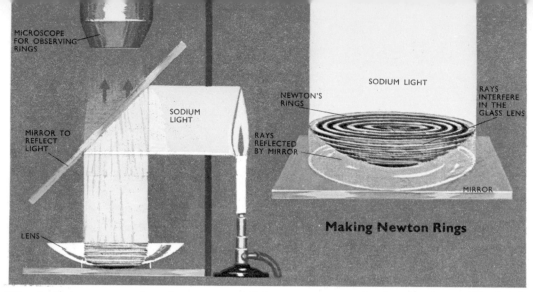

The dark rings occur when the two parts of the wave are completely out of step. The bright parts are where the waves are in step. There is only one wavelength present, so there are no rainbow-like effects.

dark rings. There are no other colours to complicate matters and 'fuzz' the fringes.

Another practicable method of producing visible interference effects is to reflect a beam of light onto a very thin wedge of glass. Some of the light is reflected by the first glass surface the beam meets, and the rest travels through the glass, is reflected at the second surface of the wedge and back out of the glass again.

When the light beam is reflected at the second surface, within the glass, it automatically changes its *phase* so that 'ups' striking the surface, are reflected as 'downs'.

This second light beam has travelled an extra distance through the glass, so its waves lag slightly behind the waves reflected at the first glass surface. If this extra distance is a half wavelength of the light or $1\frac{1}{2}$, $2\frac{1}{2}$, $3\frac{1}{2}$ . . . and so on, wavelengths (an

The incident beam of light is divided into two as part is reflected at the first surface, and part at the second.

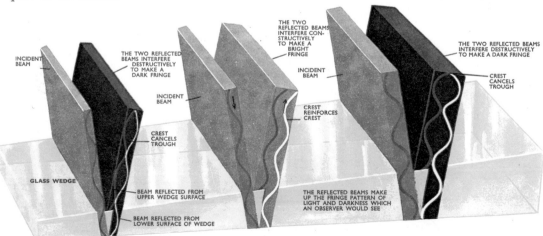

extra half is added as a result of the phase change on reflection making a total effective path difference of 1, 2, 3 wavelengths), the light beams interfere constructively. If the extra difference is a whole wavelength or multiples of a whole wavelength the beams interfere destructively. Points where the extra distance is the same will be points where the wedge has the same thickness. The wedge appears to have narrow stripes on it, where the light reflected from the glass (this is of course what we see when we look at the glass) has interfered destructively and constructively. The stripes are called *interference fringes*.

Interference fringes can be made a measurable distance apart. Since this distance depends directly on the wavelength of light used, measurement (with a low-power microscope) of the distance between light and dark lines serves as a means of measuring the wavelength of light.

CHAPTER TWENTY-NINE

Fresnel's Biprism

ONE of the characteristics of all waves is that they can be made to interfere (i.e. two crests will add together and a crest and a trough will cancel out). Single wavelength light waves such as yellow light waves from a single slit source pass through two slits and fall on a screen. If the light waves from each slit are in step (crest to crest), a bright region appears at that point. If they are out of step (crest to trough) a region of darkness results.

At the centre of the screen the light waves have both travelled exactly the same distance from each slit, so they are in step. If the yellow light is of wavelength 5000 Å (1Å = 10^{-8} cm.) then on moving out on the screen from the centre a point is reached where the **distances to each slit differ by 2500 Å. At this point crest meets trough and there is a *dark fringe*. Going out further, the difference to** the slits = 5000 Å and light from the two slits adds together to give a *bright fringe.* This is how an interference

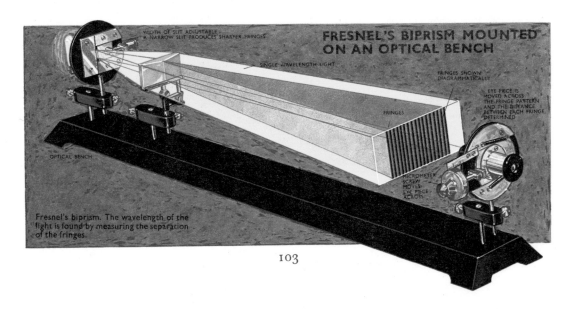

WIDTH OF SLIT ADJUSTABLE - A NARROW SLIT PRODUCES SHARPER FRINGES

SINGLE WAVELENGTH LIGHT

FRESNEL'S BIPRISM MOUNTED ON AN OPTICAL BENCH

FRINGES SHOWN DIAGRAMMATICALLY

EYE PIECE IS MOVED ACROSS THE FRINGE PATTERN AND THE DISTANCE BETWEEN EACH FRINGE DETERMINED

FRINGES

OPTICAL BENCH

MICROMETER SCREW MOVES EYE PIECE ACROSS

Fresnel's biprism. The wavelength of the light is found by measuring the separation of the fringes.

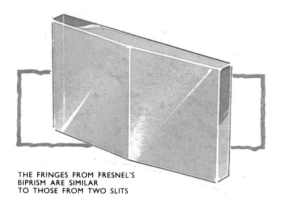

THE FRINGES FROM FRESNEL'S BIPRISM ARE SIMILAR TO THOSE FROM TWO SLITS

double slit and produces a similar pattern to a double slit. One side of the biprism is flat and the other side is cut as two planes whose faces are not quite at 180° to each other. The light passing through the flat side meets the inclined planes. These refract the two halves so that they fall on one another and interfere. If the line of the refracted beams is produced back, a person looking along these beams through the prism will 'see' two slits.

The fringes produced by these two virtual slits are very sharp and either can be viewed on a screen or through an eyepiece. To measure the wavelength of the light the eyepiece is provided with a micrometer screw so that it can be moved across the fringes and their distance apart determined. In an experiment with this prism, the wavelength of the light used is determined by measuring the width of a block of 20 fringes, and calculating from this, the average width of one fringe.

pattern is formed. Obviously the distance between the fringes depends on the wavelength of the light.

Auguste Fresnel (1788–1827), an early French experimenter in optics, explored interference effects mathematically some years after Thomas Young had demonstrated the wave nature of light. He devised a special type of twin prism called a *biprism* for producing interference effects from a single slit instead of two. This prism causes the light to *appear to come* from a

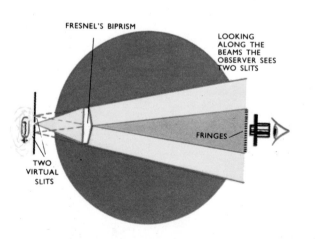

Path of the light rays in Fresnel's biprism. A person looking back through the prism, will see two imaginary slits.

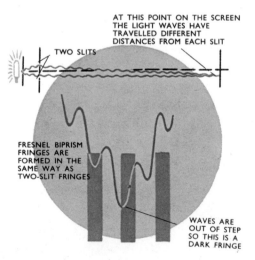

THE TWO-SLIT PATTERN

Interference fringes are due to the adding or cancellation of light waves.

CHAPTER THIRTY

Inspecting Surfaces

IN optics, the word 'fringe' invariably refers to *interference fringes*. This is the name given to the patterns of light and shade produced when the waves forming one beam of light *interfere* with the waves forming another beam of light.

Waves are successions of crests and troughs. When the crest of one beam coincides with the crest of another, the strength of the beam is increased at this particular point. However, when crest coincides with trough, the two beams virtually annihilate each other. Where crest coincides with crest on a screen, it produces a bright spot of light. Where crest coincides with trough, there is darkness.

In many industries it is necessary to examine surfaces for minute irregularities. For instance, the surfaces of ball-bearings and piston rings should be as flat as possible, and the edges of

cutting tools should be perfectly sharp and straight. Interference fringes form the basis of methods of accurate inspection of surfaces. The *surface-finish microscope* is an instrument in which interference fringes are produced and used to inspect surfaces. With it, bumps in the surface of less than a millionth of an inch can be detected and measured.

To produce visible interference fringes, the first thing needed is a single source of light and a means of splitting it into two (or more) parts.

In the surface-finish microscope the single source of light is a mercury-vapour lamp. The light is passed through a colour filter, which removes all but one of the wave-lengths of light emitted by the lamp. The light, which is now monochromatic, eventually strikes the surface under inspection. However, fixed above the

Part of the light from the mercury vapour lamp is reflected by the comparator plate, and part by the metal surface under inspection. The two parts interfere when they recombine at the comparator plate. The diagram on the left shows the interference pattern produced by two absolutely flat surfaces.

A scratch in the surface distorts the interference fringes. Each fringe joins points where the distance between the surfaces is the same. At each point along the dark fringe, the extra distance travelled by one wave has made it half a wave out of step with the other light wave.

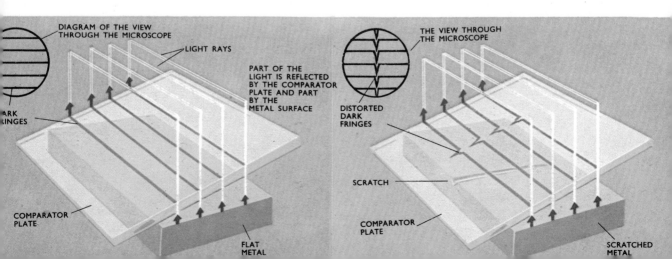

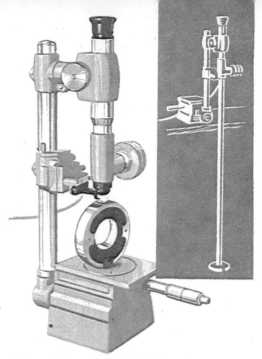

Using the surface finish microscope to examine a cylindrical surface (left) and (right) to check that the ends of a long metal bar are flat.

flat surface is a small plate of specially coated glass, a *comparator plate*.

Only about half the light from the source reaches the metal surface. Half of the light is reflected at the lower surface of the comparator plate. Light reflected at this surface and light reflected at the inspected surface form the beams which are to give the interference patterns. By travelling the extra distance from the comparator plate and back, the waves of one beam have become out of step with the waves of the other beam. The crests in one beam do not necessarily coincide with the crests in the other beam.

If the waves are half a wavelength out of step by the time they recombine at the comparator plate, crest cancels out trough, and makes a dark spot.

The amount by which the beams are out of step depends on the extra distance they have travelled between the two surfaces. All the beams which have travelled the same extra distance will be the same amount out of step. This means that all the beams which are half a wavelength out of step form a dark line, or dark fringe. If both plates are absolutely flat, and inclined at a small angle to each other, the fringe is a straight dark line.

The same happens if the waves are $1\frac{1}{2}$, $2\frac{1}{2}$ (and so on) wavelengths out of step. All the fringes are parallel to each other.

The bright fringe in between the dark fringes marks the place where the two beams have reinforced each other. The first bright fringe occurs when the two beams are one wavelength out of step. This fringe lies between the dark fringes for beams $\frac{1}{2}$ a wavelength and $1\frac{1}{2}$ wavelengths out of step. Similar bright fringes will be formed when the waves are whole numbers of wave-lengths out of step.

A consideration of the geometry of the problem shows that the fringes are all parallel to the line where the planes of the two plates (i.e. the plane of the comparator plate and the plane of the surface) meet.

In general the fringes are very closely spaced. They need to be viewed with the microscope.

A fringe is like a contour line on a map. It is a line joining all points where the distance between lower surface of the comparator plate and the metal surface under inspection is the same. So if there is a slight bump on the metal surface, the contour lines are distorted. The amount of distortion can be measured, and the height of the bump can be determined.

There are many variations of this method which enable all shapes of surface – curved, cylindrical or spherical – to be examined.

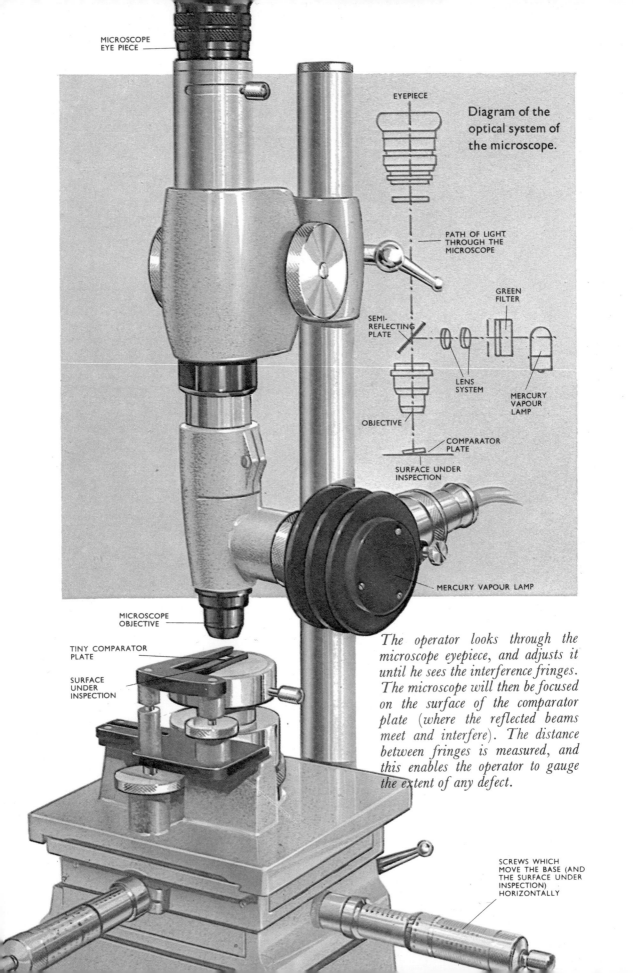

MICROSCOPE
EYE PIECE

**Diagram of the
optical system of
the microscope.**

EYEPIECE

PATH OF LIGHT
THROUGH THE
MICROSCOPE

GREEN
FILTER

SEMI-
REFLECTING
PLATE

LENS
SYSTEM

MERCURY
VAPOUR
LAMP

OBJECTIVE

COMPARATOR
PLATE

SURFACE UNDER
INSPECTION

MERCURY VAPOUR LAMP

MICROSCOPE
OBJECTIVE

TINY COMPARATOR
PLATE

SURFACE
UNDER
INSPECTION

*The operator looks through the
microscope eyepiece, and adjusts it
until he sees the interference fringes.
The microscope will then be focused
on the surface of the comparator
plate (where the reflected beams
meet and interfere). The distance
between fringes is measured, and
this enables the operator to gauge
the extent of any defect.*

SCREWS WHICH
MOVE THE BASE (AND
THE SURFACE UNDER
INSPECTION)
HORIZONTALLY

CHAPTER THIRTY-ONE

Diffraction

IF part of a beam of light is obstructed, it casts shadows. The shadows are sharp if all the rays originate from the same source of light because the unobstructed rays of light appear to travel on in straight lines. The area of shade formed by the obstruction is called the *geometrical shadow*.

However, although light does take the shortest path in travelling between two points (*i.e.* light usually travels in straight lines), it is not simply a straight line stream of energy. Light is a kind of *wave motion*, vibrating up and down and from side to side as it travels forward. This fact makes a difference to the way light casts shadows, although under normal circumstances the difference is too small to be noticed.

Other kinds of waves make areas of 'light' and 'shade' when they encounter an obstacle. Water waves, for example, trying to enter an opening

Water waves spread out from a narrow gap. The narrower the gap, the greater the proportion of diffracted waves. Huygen's construction (below) shows how the shape of the wave after diffraction can be found by drawing semicircles around each point in the gap.

in a harbour wall, do not continue in a straight line and the waves appear to spread out from the opening into the shadow of the harbour walls. This spreading out is called

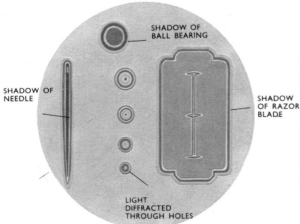

Coloured diffraction fringes around the edges of shadows of objects illuminated by a point source of light.

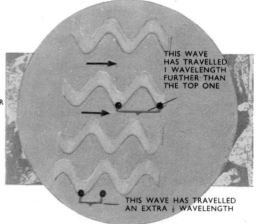

When the light waves shown above meet at a point on a screen, the top two will add together, the bottom two will cancel out.

diffraction.

Waves spread out from a point source, such as a disturbance in the surface, of water, the crests of the waves forming ever-increasing circles around the disturbance. Putting an obstacle in the path of a water wave stops part of it, but in the places where the wave is not obstructed, the waves appear to *start again*. Each point in the gap acts as though it were a water disturbance, emitting circular water waves. The shape of the crests of the waves can be found by drawing circles around every point in the gap. (Actually only semi-circles need to be drawn since it is safe to assume that the wave does not travel backwards.) If the gap is fairly large, adding together the disturbances in the middle of the gap gives a wave of the same shape it had before hitting the obstacle. But at the edges the disturbances spread out into the geometrical shadow.

Light always does this every time it meets an opaque obstacle. If a large amount of the light is allowed to carry on, the diffracted light at the edges will represent only a tiny fraction of the total light, and will be unnoticeable. This is so if light passes through a large hole. However as the size of the hole gets smaller, the proportion of diffracted light increases, since a greater proportion of it is near an edge. A very small hole acts like a single point source of light, with nearly all the light diffracted. The image of a bright and narrow slit has a diffuse area of light around it.

Diffraction of a water wave is easy to see because the waves can be identified at all points of their path. Light waves, on the other hand, can be observed only at the point where

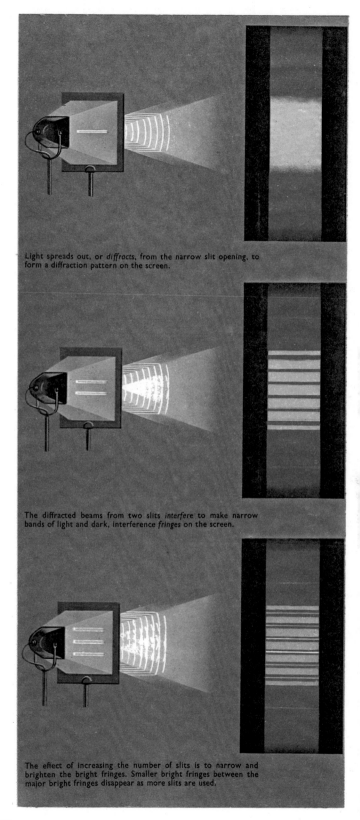

Light spreads out, or *diffracts*, from the narrow slit opening, to form a diffraction pattern on the screen.

The diffracted beams from two slits *interfere* to make narrow bands of light and dark, interference *fringes* on the screen.

The effect of increasing the number of slits is to narrow and brighten the bright fringes. Smaller bright fringes between the major bright fringes disappear as more slits are used.

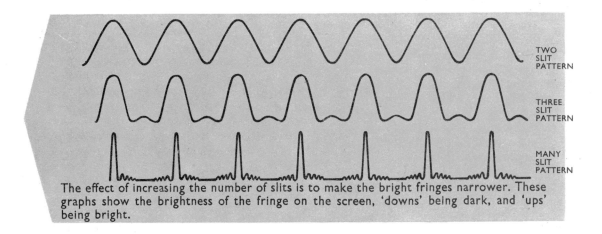

The effect of increasing the number of slits is to make the bright fringes narrower. These graphs show the brightness of the fringe on the screen, 'downs' being dark, and 'ups' being bright.

they hit something, a screen for example. And the waves vibrate too quickly and travel too fast for individual waves to be seen. The best way of observing diffraction of light is by making the different rays of light *interfere*.

It has already been shown that two monochromatic rays of light, *i.e.*, one-colour, one wavelength light meeting so that the crests of one coincide with the crests of the other reinforce each other (*interfere constructively*), while if a crest coincides

with a trough, the two waves cancel each other (*interfere destructively*) to make a dark spot.

Two narrow slits (illuminated by the same monochromate source of light so that the crests and troughs of the light going through each slit start off together) give two highly diffracted beams of light. The shadow of the slits is very different from the geometrical shadow. Light spreading out from one slit interferes with light spreading out from the other. The two beams may travel different dis-

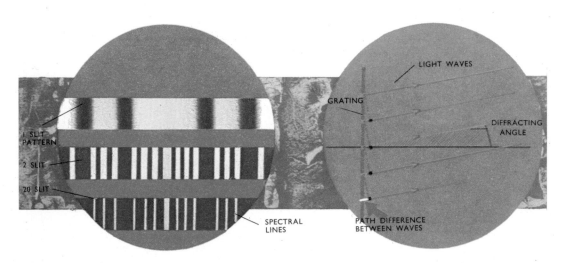

Diffraction patterns formed on a screen by a parallel beam of sodium light passing through different numbers of slits.

Diagram showing how the path difference between light rays from neighbouring slits depends on the diffracting angle.

tances before meeting at the screen, so that the crests of one do not necessarily coincide with the crests of the other. Where crest and crest coincide on the screen is a path of light, and where crest and trough coincide is a patch of darkness. The patches of light and darkness are called *interference fringes*.

When there are three narrow, equally spaced slits, the interference pattern, instead of getting more complicated, actually becomes more distinct. The extra slit imposes an extra condition for the three beams of light all to interfere constructively at the same place. This has the effect of narrowing down the bright region, at the same time making it brighter, since all the light is concentrated into it.

Adding more and more very narrow, equally spaced slits results in very much brighter and narrower bright fringes. The position of a bright fringe on the screen depends on its colour, *i.e.* wavelength. So different colours are 'focused' at different places on the screen. If instead of being illuminated by monochromatic light, the slit is lit by a mixture of all the different colours, or *white light*, the light is split up into its different colours in much the same way as it is split up by a prism.

When there are a tremendous number of slits – about 30,000 – the slits form what is called a *diffraction grating*. The slits can be the spaces between very fine, equally spaced opaque lines on a piece of glass. The lines are ruled with high precision, the 30,000 or so lines on a grating only about three inches wide. The spectra which can be obtained with these gratings are far more precise than the spectra from prisms, so diffraction gratings are often used, instead of prisms in spectroscopes.

The main difference between gratings and prisms is if, say, the grating is illuminated by white light, it gives a number of complete spectra (from red to violet), where the prism would give only one. Each line corresponds

This special source emits a mixture of red and blue light. One beam of this light continues undeviated, but in the beams deviated to each side the red light (of longer wavelength) is deviated more than the blue, forming a spectrum on each side. If a white source had been used the spectrum would have included all the shades present in the rainbow.

For clarity only one spectrum each side has been shown. Most gratings produce several spectra on each side but they can be made to concentrate the light into the first only and to suppress the second, as shown.

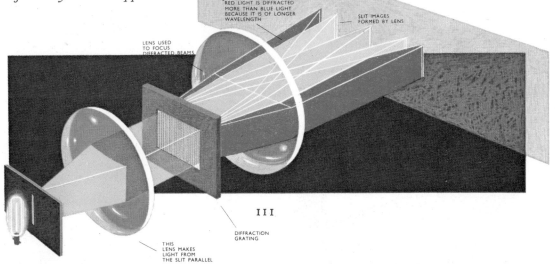

RED LIGHT IS DIFFRACTED
MORE THAN BLUE LIGHT
BECAUSE IT IS OF LONGER
WAVELENGTH

SLIT IMAGES
FORMED BY LENS

LENS USED
TO FOCUS
DIFFRACTED BEAMS

III

DIFFRACTION
GRATING

THIS
LENS MAKES
LIGHT FROM
THE SLIT PARALLEL

to a bright 'fringe' in the diffraction pattern for two slits.

Making Diffraction Gratings

How is it possible to rule 30,000 lines to the inch? The first good diffraction gratings were made in 1882 by the physicist Henry Rowland, who made a machine which could, using a diamond bit, rule 14,000 lines to the inch on glass. The diamond point was moved by means of a very fine screw. The parts of the glass which had not been ruled let the light through and acted as slits. There are still very few machines in the world which can rule a very accurate diffraction grating. Nowadays, most gratings are made by pouring plastic on an original ruled one, and making a replica mould grating. The width of a slit in a grating does not matter, so long as it is fairly small. Reducing the distance between the slits has the effect of spreading the lines further apart.

Sometimes lines appear in the spectra for which no explanation can be found, except that they are due to irregularities in the manufacture of the grating. These are called 'ghosts'. When the light is passed through a grating it is called a *transmission grating*. The other type of grating is a *reflection grating*, made by ruling a set of lines on aluminium film on glass. The spaces that have not been ruled reflect the light, and act as illuminated slits. Some gratings are made concave. They focus their own spectra. These are used for ultra-violet light, as glass lenses are opaque to ultra-violet light. Gratings are very delicate, and must be kept free from dust. To function properly, they must be used at constant temperature.

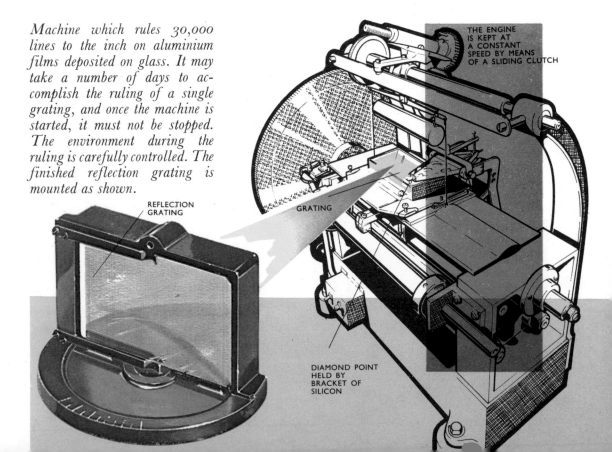

Machine which rules 30,000 lines to the inch on aluminium films deposited on glass. It may take a number of days to accomplish the ruling of a single grating, and once the machine is started, it must not be stopped. The environment during the ruling is carefully controlled. The finished reflection grating is mounted as shown.

REFLECTION GRATING

THE ENGINE IS KEPT AT A CONSTANT SPEED BY MEANS OF A SLIDING CLUTCH

GRATING

DIAMOND POINT HELD BY BRACKET OF SILICON

CHAPTER THIRTY-TWO

Rayleigh's Criterion

IT is impossible to design and make a perfect optical instrument. The optical components – lenses and mirrors – invariably have defects and the designer has to bear this in mind and try to create an instrument in which the effect of these is as small as possible. The effects of the most important shortcomings in lenses (chromatic and spherical aberration) have been largely eliminated in more refined pieces of optical equipment. But even when all possible care has been taken in designing an expensive instrument a fundamental defect remains. This results from the wave properties of light itself, and it occurs as a result of *diffraction* – the break up of light wave fronts that creates interference patterns.

This has an effect on *resolving power*. For example, if two small bright spots are being observed through a microscope, how far apart must they be before they appear as two separate spots and not as a single blurred image? Assuming that there is no aberration or other optical defect in the system, the degree of resolution is finally decided by the diffraction effects in the images of the two spots.

An image is formed because light, which is given out in all directions, is collected by the lenses of the instrument. The lenses make the light converge and bring together all the light that originated from a single object point at a single image point. Suppose the point object is a brightly illuminated, tiny spot on a dark background. This is giving out trains of light waves

in all directions, each light 'ray' consisting of a series of 'crests' and 'troughs'. Some of the waves will be collected by, say, the central region of the lens, others by the outer regions. The lens brings together all of these rays to form the spot image. To form a replica of the small spot image, the waves passing through all the different parts of the lens must arrive in step – crest reinforcing crest, trough reinforcing trough. Away from the image spot there should be no light at all. Any crests that arrive there should be cancelled out by troughs.

This is the theoretical ideal, but it never happens in practice. Not all the light waves that arrive in the image plane outside the central spot are cancelled out by other out-of-step waves. Diffraction patterns result with alternate dark and light rings

An image of the single bright spot is formed by the lens. Diffraction effects give the image a set of circular alternate light and dark rings around the central bright spot. (Inset) Light falls on each part of the image from all directions. In a bright region the light waves reinforce each other, in dark regions they cancel each other out.

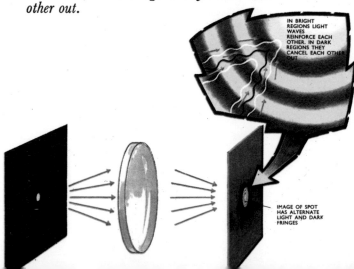

IN BRIGHT REGIONS LIGHT WAVES REINFORCE EACH OTHER, IN DARK REGIONS THEY CANCEL EACH OTHER OUT

IMAGE OF SPOT HAS ALTERNATE LIGHT AND DARK FRINGES

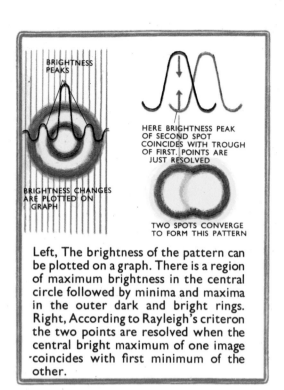

Left, The brightness of the pattern can be plotted on a graph. There is a region of maximum brightness in the central circle followed by minima and maxima in the outer dark and bright rings. Right, According to Rayleigh's criteron the two points are resolved when the central bright maximum of one image coincides with first minimum of the other.

formed outside the central image spot.

The existence of these outer rings spoils the resolution of an instrument. If two object points are viewed through an instrument they will not be resolved if they are too close together. If the separation is increased the image separates into two image points.

It is desirable to be able to say definitely at what separation objects are being resolved by an instrument – this is a measure of the resolving power of the instrument. Lord Rayleigh suggested an arbitrary criterion for this. In the *Rayleigh criterion* two points are said to be resolved if the centre of the bright central disc coincides with the dark ring around the neighbouring image spot. If the image points are closer than this, they are unresolved.

CHAPTER THIRTY-THREE

The Phase Contrast Microscope

WITH a normal microscope transparent objects like the amoeba must be stained to make them visible. This can be a serious drawback, for it sometimes interferes with a particular process being studied. To overcome this problem the *phase contrast* microscope has been developed; it enables transparent objects to be seen under conditions of high magnification without staining.

The Phase Contrast Principle

Light is transmitted in the form of electro-magnetic waves. The *wavelength* of light of a particular colour is the distance between successive 'crests' and 'troughs' in the wave train. The intensity of the light depends on the 'height' (amplitude) of the waves. The greater the wave amplitude, the brighter the source of light will appear to an observer.

Suppose in an ordinary microscope that the specimen is illuminated evenly by light collected by the condenser. Different parts of the specimen absorb different amounts of light so the light waves coming from the different parts are of different amplitude. Light waves passing through a 'dense' part of the specimen will be reduced in amplitude more than those passing through a less 'dense' part. The light waves are brought to focus by the optical system of the microscope, and produce an image. Those parts of the image formed by the waves of small amplitude produce a dimmer effect in the image, and so those regions appear darker. For example, the nucleus of an amoeba absorbs more light than its surroundings and shows up as a dark blob against a lighter background. The waves of large amplitude produce brighter regions in the image. All *absorbing* media reduce the amplitudes of light waves that pass through them.

On the other hand, a transparent medium does not reduce the wave amplitude. Or if it does, not enough to be detected by the human eye. But it does something else to the wave – it slows it down. As a result of the slowing down, the wave undergoes a *change of phase*. This may be explained in the following way.

Two light beams, originating from one lamp, pass along two different paths, side by side. One path is in vacuum, in the other there is a film of transparent material, say glass. Both the emerging light beams will *appear* identical because the wave amplitudes are both unaffected. But, when a 'crest' of the wave is still in the glass, the crest will have gone past in the vacuum path. The difference between the positions of the two crests is the *phase difference* between the two transmitted waves.

Although the eye can detect a difference in wave amplitude, it cannot detect a phase difference.

The trick used in the phase contrast microscope is to detect *phase differences* between light waves that have passed through transparent objects and convert them into amplitude differences. For example, not only is the nucleus of the amoeba visible, but structures in the surrounding protoplasm, not visible under ordinary microscope, are shown up.

To see how this is done, the way that an ordinary microscope forms its image must first be understood. This

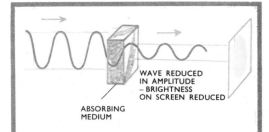

ABSORBING MEDIUM

WAVE REDUCED IN AMPLITUDE – BRIGHTNESS ON SCREEN REDUCED

When light passes through an absorbing medium, the light waves are reduced in amplitude. The light patch on the screen is *reduced* in brightness.

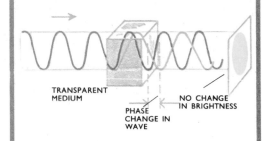

TRANSPARENT MEDIUM

PHASE CHANGE IN WAVE

NO CHANGE IN BRIGHTNESS

When light is passed through the transparent medium, the waves are unchanged in amplitude but altered in phase. The patch on the screen is unchanged in brightness – the phase change does not affect this.

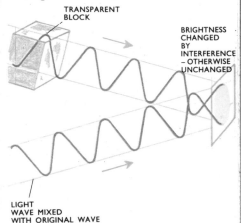

TRANSPARENT BLOCK

BRIGHTNESS CHANGED BY INTERFERENCE – OTHERWISE UNCHANGED

LIGHT WAVE MIXED WITH ORIGINAL WAVE

The phase change due to the transparent block does not affect the brightness of the patch on the screen. It can be shown up, however, by 'mixing' the transmitted light with light of the same wavelength but half a wavelength out of step. Interference then takes place so that a darker patch appears on the screen.

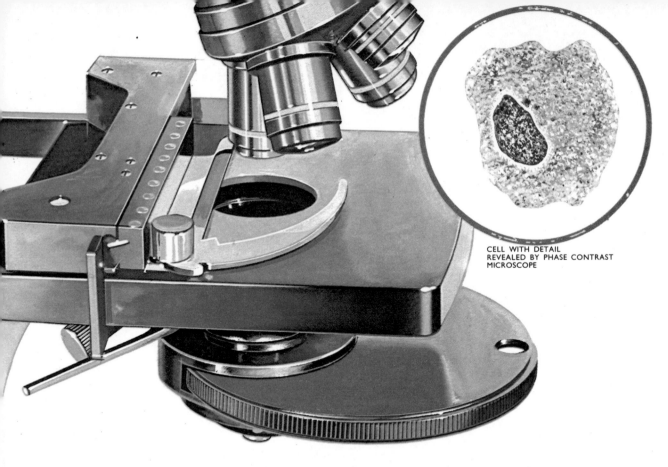

CELL WITH DETAIL
REVEALED BY PHASE CONTRAST
MICROSCOPE

A typical phase contrast microscope. The microscope can be used in the ordinary way and the diaphragm can be brought into operation and adjusted. The zone plate is brought into operation with the appropriate objective lens and the focus adjusted. Special illumination has to be employed to obtain good results with phase contrast microscopes.

was explained by the German physicist E. Abbe, in the last century. He explained image formation as a *diffraction effect*. He suggested that instead of simply thinking of single light waves, reduced in amplitude when passed through an absorbing medium, *two* sets of light waves must be considered. One is the original wave (the *incident* wave). This passes on through the specimen unhindered and unaltered in amplitude. Then there is the second wave, the *diffracted* wave. This is one that is scattered and thrown away from the absorbing object. But it eventually meets up with the incident wave at the image. When it does so, it *interferes* with the incident wave, re-

ducing the brightness at that part of the image. To do this the diffracted wave must be one half wavelength out of step with the incident wave. A crest in the incident wave must coincide with a trough in the diffracted wave, so the second wave (partially, at any rate) cancels out the first. The less absorbent the specimen, the smaller the diffracted wave, so the less is the cancellation.

In a transparent medium, there are also two waves, incident and diffracted, but the diffracted wave is not sufficiently out of phase with the incident wave to affect the brightness of the image when the two waves come together at the image. In the

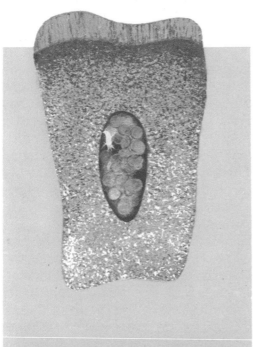

Using the light microscope very little cellular detail can be observed in the unstained material. The protoplasm is colourless as are most of the structures within it. However, with staining techniques it is possible to preserve many of the cell constituents so that they are visible. Fixing and staining processes involve killing the cell, however, and there must necessarily be considerable distortion of the living architecture. With the phase contrast microscope however, it is possible to view living cells in considerable detail.

phase contrast microscope, the diffracted wave is extracted, and made so that it is one *half-wavelength* out of step with the incident wave. It interferes with the incident wave, and the transparent specimen shows up with all its detail as if it were an absorbing specimen.

The Phase Contrast System

In the phase contrast microscope, the diffracted and incident light is separated, using a circular diaphragm that contains an open circular ring

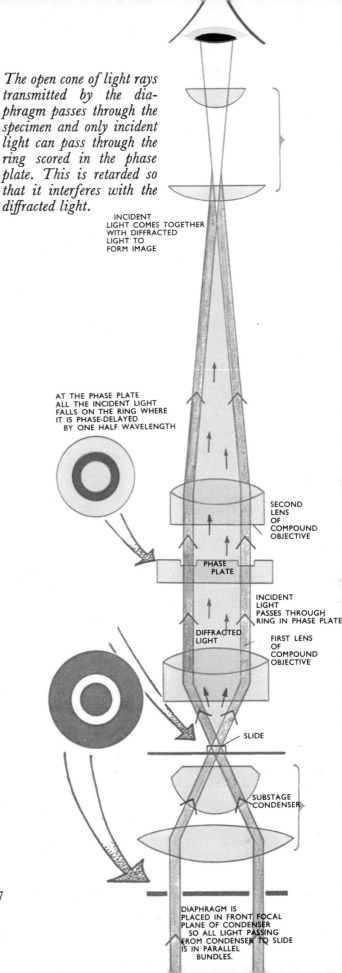

The open cone of light rays transmitted by the diaphragm passes through the specimen and only incident light can pass through the ring scored in the phase plate. This is retarded so that it interferes with the diffracted light.

INCIDENT LIGHT COMES TOGETHER WITH DIFFRACTED LIGHT TO FORM IMAGE

AT THE PHASE PLATE ALL THE INCIDENT LIGHT FALLS ON THE RING WHERE IT IS PHASE-DELAYED BY ONE HALF WAVELENGTH

SECOND LENS OF COMPOUND OBJECTIVE

PHASE PLATE

INCIDENT LIGHT PASSES THROUGH RING IN PHASE PLATE

DIFFRACTED LIGHT

FIRST LENS OF COMPOUND OBJECTIVE

SLIDE

SUBSTAGE CONDENSER

DIAPHRAGM IS PLACED IN FRONT FOCAL PLANE OF CONDENSER SO ALL LIGHT PASSING FROM CONDENSER TO SLIDE IS IN PARALLEL BUNDLES.

(*annulus*). The condenser is set up so that it passes light through the specimen in parallel bundles. The diaphragm is placed at the first focus of the condenser so that light passes through the annulus and opens out to be formed into parallel bundles by the condenser. (Light originating at a focus of a lens is made parallel when it passes through the lens). This parallel light passes through the specimen and is brought to focus by the object lens of the microscope. Now all the incident (undiffracted) light has passed as parallel bundles through the specimen and when it is brought to focus by the object lens it forms an image replica of the original annulus. This is all *undiffracted light*. The diffracted light, on the other hand, is scattered in the specimen. This fills the circle inside the annulus. So the

two sorts of light are separated in the image of the diaphragm, incident light fills the ring, the other light the disc inside the ring. All that remains is to retard the diffracted light so that it is one half wavelength out of step with the incident light. This is done by placing a *zone plate* (or diffraction plate) in the plane where the image of the diaphragm is formed. The circle of incident light falls on a ring scored in the surface of the plate. The thickness of the plate is such that no phase change is undergone by the incident light. The diffracted light passes through the rest of the plate (which is thick enough to retard the diffracted light so that it becomes one half-wavelength out of step). Then both sets of light waves form the final image, one set interfering with the

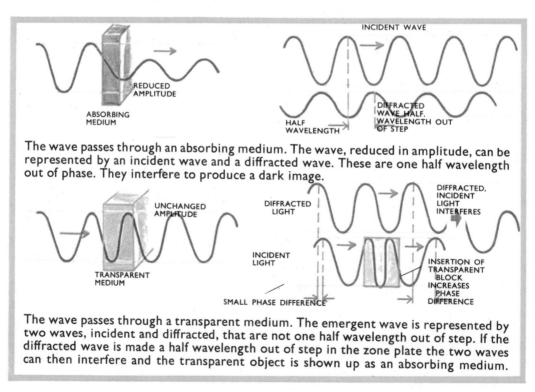

The wave passes through an absorbing medium. The wave, reduced in amplitude, can be represented by an incident wave and a diffracted wave. These are one half wavelength out of phase. They interfere to produce a dark image.

The wave passes through a transparent medium. The emergent wave is represented by two waves, incident and diffracted, that are not one half wavelength out of step. If the diffracted wave is made a half wavelength out of step in the zone plate the two waves can then interfere and the transparent object is shown up as an absorbing medium.

other to form the phase contrast image.

In use, it is desirable to be able to use the phase contrast microscope with different objective lenses. For each different lens there has to be a different diaphragm anulus, but in some models it is possible to select the anulus required by adjustment of a turret arrangement. The turret normally is supplied as a part of the substage condenser, and the phase ring as a part of the objective lens arrangement.

CHAPTER THIRTY-FOUR

Polarization

LIGHT is a form of wave motion, but as it travels at such a high speed (186,326 miles per second) it is not possible to observe the way in which the moving waves vibrate. However, a series of experiments has shown that the waves vibrate at right angles to the direction of the light beam, and because of this light is said to consist of *transverse waves*.

Since the vibration of light waves cannot be seen, it is convenient to see how other *visible* transverse waves vibrate. Such waves may be set up in a length of cord by repeatedly moving one end up and down (*i.e.* at right angles to the cord). The vibrations in the cord will pass through a narrow gap provided the longest axis of the gap is parallel to the direction of the vibrations. Thus if the cord is vibrating up and down, the motion will be transmitted through a vertical gap. However, if the cord also passes through a horizontal gap the vibrations cannot pass through this.

The cord in this example can only vibrate in one *plane* (at right angles to the direction of travel). But an ordinary beam of light consists of a great number of individual waves which are vibrating in different directions (all at right angles to the light path). But under certain conditions it is possible for all the vibrations in

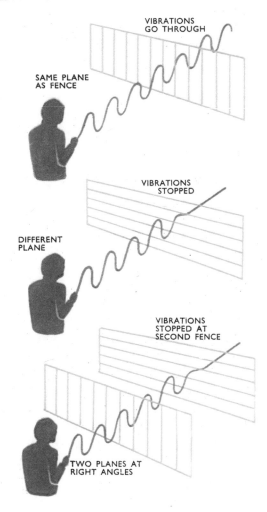

The vibrations in the cord will only pass through the narrow gap in the railings if the vibrations are parallel to the individual rails. Thus an up and down vibration is transmitted through the vertical railings, but is stopped by the horizontal ones.

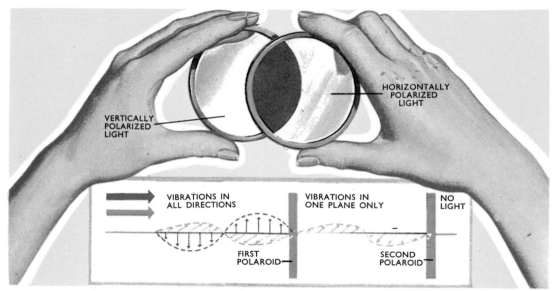

VERTICALLY POLARIZED LIGHT

HORIZONTALLY POLARIZED LIGHT

VIBRATIONS IN ALL DIRECTIONS

VIBRATIONS IN ONE PLANE ONLY

NO LIGHT

FIRST POLAROID

SECOND POLAROID

Ordinary light is made up of vibrations in many different directions at right angles to the light path. Some of this light will pass through a pair of Polaroid discs provided the 'slits' in the two discs are parallel with one another. However, if the discs are 'crossed' the polarized light transmitted from the first disc is stopped by the second one.

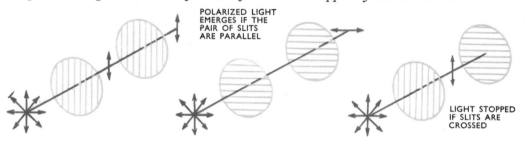

POLARIZED LIGHT EMERGES IF THE PAIR OF SLITS ARE PARALLEL

LIGHT STOPPED IF SLITS ARE CROSSED

a beam of light to be *confined to one plane* at right angles to the beam. Such a beam is said to be *polarized*.

Certain crystals, in particular transparent crystals of calcite (a form of calcium carbonate) known as *Iceland spar*, have the property of polarizing light. The ability of such crystals to polarize light can be tested by passing a ray of light through two crystals of the substance. Each crystal can be thought of as containing a number of very narrow slits parallel to each other. These 'slits' are so narrow that only the waves whose vibrations are parallel to the slits can pass through.

Thus the light emerging from the first crystal is made up of waves whose

vibrations are almost all parallel with one another. The passage of light whose plane of vibration does not correspond with the favoured plane is stopped. If the second crystal is arranged so that the 'slits' are parallel with those in the first crystal the polarized light leaving the first crystal will pass through the second crystal also. But if the second crystal is then rotated, the amount of light transmitted will be reduced until a point will be reached (at right angles to the first position) when no light is transmitted through the second crystal. In this position the waves of polarized light are vibrating at right angles to the slits, so the vibrations are unable to pass through it.

Light can be polarized by *reflection* as well as by refraction. In fact the French physicist E. L. Malus (1775-1812) discovered this property of light after observing sunlight *reflected* from windows. Malus' discovery can best be illustrated by means of a simple experiment. Two mirrors are arranged parallel to each other, forming a kind of periscope. When one of the mirrors is *rotated* it is found that the amount of light reflected from the second mirror gradually decreases to a minimum (it disappears completely in one particular position—but this is very difficult to attain) and then increases again. What is happening is that on reflection at the first mirror the vibrations in *all but one plane* are absorbed. In other words, the reflected beam is *polarized*. How completely the light is polarized depends on the *angle of incidence*.

As the proportion of light reflected from a surface is quite small, this is not a very profitable method of obtaining polarized light, so light is usually polarized by refraction. One quite satisfactory polarizing medium has been *manufactured* and is marketed under the 'Polaroid' trade name. It comprises a cellulose nitrate film containing very small crystals of iodoquinine sulphate. In manufacture, these tiny crystals are made to line themselves up in one direction so that they behave like crystals of Iceland spar.

'Polaroid' discs can be used to produce polarized light in much the same way as with other polarizing media. If ordinary light enters the film, the light emerging is polarized —almost all vibrations at right angles to the favoured direction have been absorbed. That the light has been

polarized can be shown by rotating a second 'Polaroid' disc in the path of the light emerging from the first. As the second disc is rotated a point is reached where virtually no light is transmitted—the greatest amount of light is transmitted when the disc is at right angles to this position. Polaroid has many uses, not the least of which is in sun glasses. With these the glare caused by the sun's light

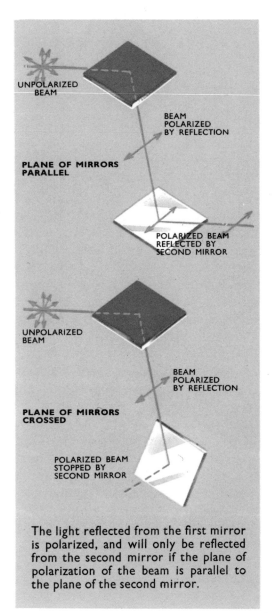

UNPOLARIZED BEAM

BEAM POLARIZED BY REFLECTION

PLANE OF MIRRORS PARALLEL

POLARIZED BEAM REFLECTED BY SECOND MIRROR

UNPOLARIZED BEAM

BEAM POLARIZED BY REFLECTION

PLANE OF MIRRORS CROSSED

POLARIZED BEAM STOPPED BY SECOND MIRROR

The light reflected from the first mirror is polarized, and will only be reflected from the second mirror if the plane of polarization of the beam is parallel to the plane of the second mirror.

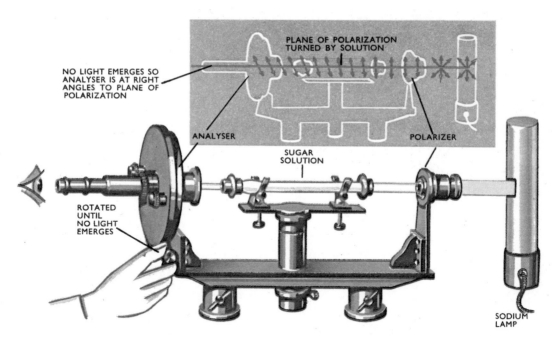

NO LIGHT EMERGES SO
ANALYSER IS AT RIGHT
ANGLES TO PLANE OF
POLARIZATION

PLANE OF POLARIZATION
TURNED BY SOLUTION

ANALYSER

SUGAR
SOLUTION

POLARIZER

ROTATED
UNTIL
NO LIGHT
EMERGES

SODIUM
LAMP

The plane of polarization of the sodium light from the polarizer is rotated as it passes through a solution of an 'optically active' substance such as sucrose. The extent of the rotation is determined by rotating the analyser until no light reaches the observer. The 'slits' in the analyser are then at right angles to the final plane of polarization.

being reflected from the road or water surfaces, etc., is considerably reduced. The reflected light is already polarized so that only that portion of the light which is polarized in the favoured direction is transmitted through the 'Polaroid' disc.

Solutions of various sugars, including cane sugar (sucrose) and of certain other organic substances have the property of *rotating the plane of polarization* of light passed through them. The extent of the rotation is measured with an apparatus called a *polarimeter* or *saccharimeter*. This comprises a source of monochromatic (one coloured) light – usually a sodium lamp, a means of polarizing the light (a *polarizer*), a tube to hold the sample, and a means of checking the plane of polarization (an *analyser*).

To use the apparatus the tube is first filled with water, the lamp switched on and the analyser rotated until no light is seen to emerge from it. The polarizer and analyser are then said to be *crossed*. The water in the tube is then replaced by the solution under test. The analyser is again rotated until it is again crossed, and the angle through which the plane of polarization has been rotated is then noted. Some substances (*e.g. d*-glucose, grape sugar) cause the plane of polarization to rotate in a clockwise or right-handed sense. These are said to be *dextrorotatory. Laevorotatory* substances (*l*-fructose, 'fruit' sugar) cause the plane of polarization to be rotated in an anti-clockwise or left-handed sense. Such information provides clues to the structure of these compounds. The amount of rotation indicates the strength of the solution.

Photo-Electric Effect

CHAPTER THIRTY-FIVE

The Photo-Electric Effect

THE photographer's light meter tells him how intense the light is. On a dull day, the pointer on the meter dial will indicate a low reading, and on a bright day, the reading will be correspondingly higher. This light meter is working because of the *photoelectric effect*. As its name suggests, this effect links light (*photo*) and electricity. Light striking the meter produces an electric current, by knocking electrons out of a plate of the sensitive metal selenium inside the meter. A flow of negatively-charged electrons constitutes an electric current, and in fact the pointer on the light meter is part of an instrument which registers current-flow, a *galvanometer*.

Electrons are the loosely-bound parts of atoms, and the most loosely bound of them are not very difficult to dislodge. For instance, when a difference in electrical potential, or *voltage*, is put across the ends of a copper wire, the outermost electrons easily become dislodged and drift through the wire. But it is not so obvious why light should do the same thing.

There are several interesting features about the photoelectric effect. In the first place, the more intense the beam of light, the bigger the current of released electrons. This is why it can be used to measure the intensity of light in a light meter. But the strength of the photoelectric current also depends on the colour of

When a lump of potassium is bombarded with yellow light, no photoelectric electrons are released.

But even a weak beam of blue light is able to release a photoelectric current from potassium . . . . .

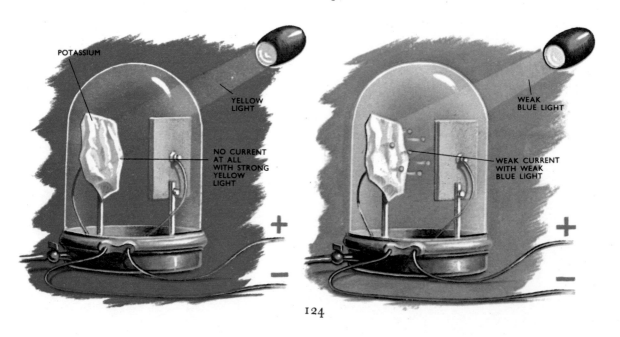

POTASSIUM

YELLOW LIGHT

NO CURRENT AT ALL WITH STRONG YELLOW LIGHT

WEAK BLUE LIGHT

WEAK CURRENT WITH WEAK BLUE LIGHT

+

−

light striking the sensitive surface in a rather peculiar way.

Selenium is used for light meters because it responds to visible light. But it does not respond to infra-red light i.e. to light of *longer wavelength* than visible light. All forms of light are wave-like disturbances, and different wavelengths of light are interpreted by the human brain as different colours. The shortest visible waves are the waves of violet light. Indigo, blue, green, yellow, orange, and red waves have progressively longer wavelengths. Infra-red rays have even longer wavelengths. Whether or not a photoelectric current is emitted depends on the wavelength of the light.

The early experiments in photoelectricity were conducted with two copper plates (one of which corresponded to the selenium in the light meter), placed inside an evacuated glass bulb. One of the plates was illuminated, and the photoelectric current from

. . . while a stronger blue beam releases a larger current. The threshold for potassium lies in the green part of the spectrum.

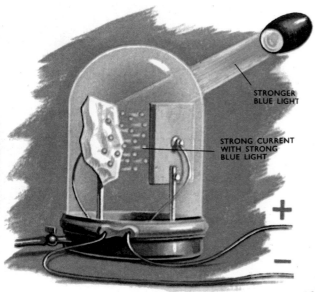

STRONGER
BLUE LIGHT

STRONG CURRENT
WITH STRONG
BLUE LIGHT

+

–

it was measured.

Copper is not as sensitive to light as selenium. In fact it does not respond at all to any visible light, but gives out a photoelectric current when even shorter wavelength waves, ultra-violet rays, are illuminating it.

The two plates were connected, through a variable resistor, to a battery supplying a difference of voltage of a few volts, and an ammeter was connected to measure the current flowing around the circuit. Of course, no current flowed when the plates were not illuminated, for the plates were separated by a sizeable gap. The current was unable to flow across the gap.

But as soon as ultra-violet light was beamed at the plate connected to the negative terminal of the battery, a current of a few micro-amps flowed around the circuit. The ultra-violet light had released electrons from the copper, and the negatively charged electrons had been attracted towards the other, positively charged, copper plate. They had been able to skip across the gap.

If, on the other hand, the *positively charged* plate were illuminated, no current would flow, even though electrons were being released. They would be repelled by the negative plate, and so would be unable to jump across the gap in the circuit.

As the beam of ultra-violet light was intensified, the current intensified too. But as soon as the wavelength was lengthened, so that visible light hit the plate, the current stopped. No matter how intense the beam of visible light, no current at all would flow.

This kind of behaviour is not limited to copper. Every single metal has what is called a *threshold*, a limiting

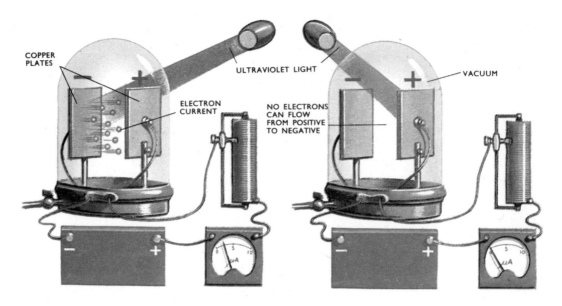

Labels in top diagram:
COPPER PLATES
ULTRAVIOLET LIGHT
VACUUM
ELECTRON CURRENT
NO ELECTRONS CAN FLOW FROM POSITIVE TO NEGATIVE

This experiment shows that light releases electrons, negatively-charged *particles, in the photoelectric effect.*

wave-length where shorter waves will produce a photoelectric effect, no matter how weak they are, and longer wave-lengths, no matter how intense, will not. For instance, the threshold of potassium is at a point in the green part of the spectrum. Blue light will produce a photoelectric effect, while yellow light will not.

Each metal has a different threshold, and this is hardly surprising, for the electrons are bound to the metals by differing forces. Electrons in some metals are easier to knock out than others. An electron is knocked out because it is given some extra energy by light rays, sufficient to overcome the forces which bind the electron to the metal. Because shorter wave-lengths are better at knocking electrons out than longer wave-lengths, the short wave-lengths of light must have more energy. The amount of energy carried by a light beam depends on the wave-length and also on the intensity of the light beam. So it might be reasoned that the electrons

In the dark no visible rays reach the eye, so nothing can be seen. However, invisible infra-red rays are coming from the object.

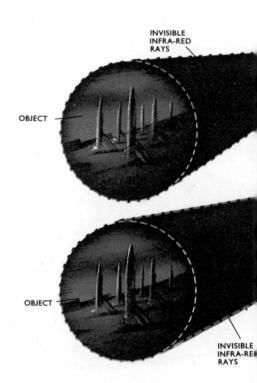

INVISIBLE INFRA-RED RAYS
OBJECT
OBJECT
INVISIBLE INFRA-RED RAYS

could be given just as much energy by an intense long wave-length beam as a less intense short wave-length beam. However, the photoelectric electrons did not behave like this.

Their queer behaviour led scientists, notably Albert Einstein, to argue that light could not be made up of continuous waves. It must arrive as separate bundles of energy, the amount of energy in each bundle depending on the wave-length of light. One bundle of light knocks out one electron, *if it has sufficient energy*. If it has less than the threshold, it cannot knock out the electron and, because light bundles are separate things, they cannot join forces to knock out a single electron.

It does not matter how many lower energy bundles strike the surface. They cannot knock a single electron completely clear. When the energy of the individual bundles is above the threshold, then each bundle will be able to knock out one electron. The more intense the beam, the greater the number of bundles, the more intense the photoelectric current. Materials like selenium are used for light meters because they have a fairly low threshold. All visible light bundles have enough energy to free their electrons. It is possible to make materials sensitive even to infra-red light, by specially coating their surfaces. If the metal caesium is oxidised in a special way and deposited on a thin layer of silver, the whole surface structure is altered, and only a small amount of energy is needed to knock out an electron. So this kind of substance can be used in instruments to record invisible infra-red light.

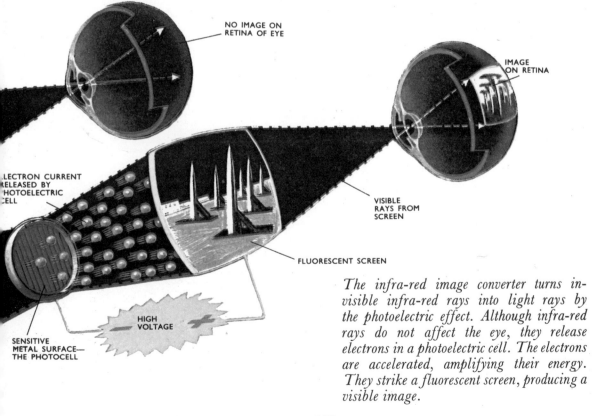

NO IMAGE ON RETINA OF EYE

IMAGE ON RETINA

ELECTRON CURRENT RELEASED BY PHOTOELECTRIC CELL

VISIBLE RAYS FROM SCREEN

FLUORESCENT SCREEN

HIGH VOLTAGE

SENSITIVE METAL SURFACE— THE PHOTOCELL

The infra-red image converter turns invisible infra-red rays into light rays by the photoelectric effect. Although infra-red rays do not affect the eye, they release electrons in a photoelectric cell. The electrons are accelerated, amplifying their energy. They strike a fluorescent screen, producing a visible image.

Index

Absorption spectra, 85, 86
Accommodation of eye, 51
Achromat, 62, 63
Air, refractive index of, 24
Annealing lehr, 55
Aperture in camera, 78–80
Astigmatism, 50, 51, 63
Astronomical telescopes, 67, 68

Biconcave lens, 29
Biconvex lens, 29
Blind spot of eye, 51
Blocking compound, 57
Box camera, 77
Burning glass, 29

Caesium, 127
Camera, 67–80
Candela, definition of, 14
Candle-power, definition of, 14
Cardinal points of lenses, 42–45
Car headlight mirror, 21
Cassegrain telescope, 67
Chromatic aberration, 30, 62, 63
Collimator of spectroscope, 83, 84
Colour filters, 91, 92
Colour mixing, 93–96
Compound microscope, 69–71
Concave lens, determining focal length of, 41
Concave meniscus lens, 29
Concave mirrors, 21, 22
  determining focal length of, 39
Constructive interference, 99
Convex lens, determining focal length of, 40, 41
Convex meniscus lens, 29
Convex mirrors, 21, 22
  determining focal length of, 39, 40
Corpuscular theory of light, 6–9
Critical angle of incidence, 26
Curved mirrors, 21, 22, 35–37, 39–42
  determining the focal length of, 39, 40

Destructive interference, 99
Dextrorotatory substances, 122
Diamond, refractive index of, 24
Diascopes, 72, 73
Diffraction, 108–114
Diffraction fringes, 108
Diffraction grating, 111, 112
Driving mirror, 22

Einstein, Albert, 7
Emission spectra, 83–86
Epidiascope, 73
Eye, defects of, 50–53

Fizeau, 10–12
Flicker photometer, 16
Focal length, determination of, 39–42
  of curved mirror, 35
  of lens, 37

Focus, in camera, 76–80
Foucault, 10–13
Fraunhofer, Joseph von, 86
Fraunhofer lines, 86
Fresnel, Auguste, 104
Fresnel's biprism, 103, 104

Galilean telescope, 67, 68
Grease spot photometer, 14

Hydrogen, emission spectrum of, 83
Hypermetropia, 52

Iceland spar, 120
Illumination, measurement of, 13–16
Images, 18–22, 28–48
  determination of, 37, 38
Incident ray, definition of, 18
Inferior mirage, 27
Infra-red image converter, 127
Interference, 8, 60, 98–107
Interference fringes, 103–106

Kaleidoscope, 19

Laevorotatory substances, 122
Lens combinations, 42–45
Lenses, 28–30, 33–63
  blooming of, 58–61
  defects of, 29, 30, 62–63
  determining the focal length of, 40, 41
  manufacture of, 54–57
  types of, 29
Light, colours of, 81–96
  measuring the intensity of, 13–16
  measuring the velocity of, 10–13
  nature of, 5–9
  reflection of, 6, 7, 18–22
  refraction of, 23–27
Light waves, diffraction of, 108–112
  interference of, 98–107
  polarization of, 119–122
Lummer-Brodhun photometer, 16

Magnesium fluoride, use of in blooming of lenses, 58–61
Malus, E. L., 121
Mercury, emission spectrum of, 83
Michelson, 10, 13
Microscope, using a, 64
Mirages, 26, 27
Mirrors, 18–22, 32–34
Monochromatic light, 101, 102
Myopia, 52

Neon, emission spectrum of, 84
Newtonian telescope, 22, 67
Newton, Sir Isaac, 7
Nodal points of lenses, 42, 43
Normal, definition of, 18

Optical bench, 46–48
Optical instruments, 65–80

Paraxial region of lenses, 45
Periscopes, 74, 75
Phase contrast microscope, 114–119
Photo-electric effect, 123–127
Photometry, 13–16
Photon theory, 7–9
Pinhole camera, 76, 77
Plane mirrors, 18–20
Planoconcave lens, 29
Planoconvex lens, 29
Polarimeter, 122
Polarized light, 119–122
Polaroid discs, 120–122
Presbyopia, 52
Primary colours of light, 93–96
'Primary' pigments, 94–96
Principal focus of curved mirror, 35
Principal focus of lens, 36, 37, 42–45
Principal plane of lenses, 42–45
Principal points of lenses, 42–45
Prisms, 28, 29, 74, 75

Rainbow, 87, 88
Rayleigh, Lord, 89, 113
Rayleigh's criterion, 113, 114
Real images, 34
Reflecting telescopes, 66–68
Reflection of light, 18–22
Refracting telescopes, 66–68
Refraction, 23–27
  index of, 24, 25
Röemer, Olaus, 10, 11

Searchlight mirror, 21
Selenium, use of in lightmeter, 125
Shadow photometer, 15
Shaving mirror, 21
Shutter, in camera, 78–80
Sight, defects of, 50–53
Sky, colour of, 89, 90
Slide projector, 72, 73
Sodium, emission spectrum of, 84
Spectra, 82–86
Spectroscopes, 83–86
Spherical aberration, 30, 63
Sunset, colour of, 89, 90
Sunshine recorder, 30
Superior mirage, 27
Surface-finish microscope, 105–107

Telescopes, 66–68
Terrestrial telescope, 66, 67
Total internal reflection, 26, 27

Virtual images, 32, 33

Water, refractive index of, 24
Wave-particle theory of light, 9
Wave theory of light, 7–9
Wax block photometer, 15